TES

YOUR

I.Q.

HAMLYN HELP YOURSELF GUIDE

TEST YOUR I.Q.

VICTOR SEREBRIAKOFF

LONDON   NEW YORK   SYDNEY   TORONTO

First published 1990
Hamlyn is an imprint of Octopus Illustrated Publishing
Michelin House, 81 Fulham Road, London SW3 6RB
part of Reed International Books

Reprinted 1991

© Copyright Reed International Books Limited 1990

This edition published 1993 by BCA
by arrangement with
HAMLYN PUBLISHING GROUP

CN 1590

Printed and bound in Great Britain
by Collins, Glasgow

Contents

1

Know Yourself

Most people are fairly happy most of the time but there are two kinds of misery which few of us avoid at some period in our lives. There is the misery that comes on that black day when you suddenly see that something you have set your heart on, that you have worked and fought for, is not going to be. You can say, 'Well I had a go, I overreached myself but at least I tried.' But the failure is bitter in the mouth, especially when you see those with less merit and more luck who have won the prize.

But worse, much worse, is the dragging, continuing misery of vain regret that comes when you underestimate yourself and do not even try. A great chance has come and gone. Then you come to see that you had more in you than you thought and could have made it. Others have run off with the prize that could have been yours if you had only known your own ability, your potential and powers.

It is important for you to know all about the one person you can never get away from – yourself. The happy ones are those who, early in life, find out their strengths and weaknesses, face facts and adjust to self-knowledge. Not for them the miseries caused by overestimating their powers and losing a long, hopeless struggle. Nor do they face the bitter 'might-have-been' torture of those who find out, too late, that they could have done much more with their talents if they had not been so modest and self-effacing.

But how can we know ourselves? How can we, with our pride, or our modesty, our self-deception and our varying moods, how can we get a fair and unbiased idea of our underlying and inborn character and potential?

With due modesty I give myself as an example. When I joined the British army in 1945 at the age of 32 I was, after a patchy career and an inadequate education, a bored, passable manual worker engaged in routine war work in a factory. The army gave me an intelligence test, asked me what on earth I thought I was doing, under-used as a wood machinist, put me down as a potential officer, promoted me, and subsequently trained and educated me. That is what gave me new hopes and ambitions. After that my whole life was transformed and, as an high-tech industrialist, inventor, writer, lecturer and Mensa pioneer, I have had a whale of a time searching for my limits and not finding them.

The soft science of psychology

The most complicated and mysterious thing in the world we know of, the most difficult thing to understand, is something that you and I have in our heads – a brain. Physics, chemistry, astronomy and the other 'exact' sciences are hard to master and very complex but they are orderly and simple compared with the intricate workings of the kilo and a half of grey spaghetti in your head. This finely tangled felt of 10,000 million nerves, each with 1,000 fibrous branches and each with countless connections, is what you are using to understand these words. So understanding yourself and your mental workings is not going to be easy. The 'hard' scientists who can measure what they see – the physicists, chemists, astronomers, those who do not deal with living things – they can sneer at the 'softness' of the imprecise sciences but their problems, difficult though they are, are as nothing compared with those facing the life scientist.

And of the problems of the life scientist the toughest, hardest problems of all are those of understanding the most complex thing of all, the one that lies in your skull and mine – the brain.

That is the bad news. Here is the good news. Psychology is a difficult science, but it is not quite an impossible one. If we look at any complex thing for long enough we can begin to notice, not at first strict laws, but regularities, invariances – things we can predict, about the way it works. We begin to be able to say in advance, not what will happen next but what is most likely to happen next, what the probabilities are. So as long as we do not look for certainty and just want to improve our powers of guesswork, psychologists can help a little. If we would like to know a bit more than we do now and base our guesses on systematic studies, the infant science of psychology can help again as it helped me in 1945.

One of the successful branches of psychology is psychometrics, the study and measurement of human mental differences. For instance, some of us are habitually matey and chummy, love company, are outgoing and impulsive, whereas others are generally more self-contained, like to have a few close friends and prefer more lonely pursuits. We all notice these things. Psychometricians can measure them carefully and without bias. The first group are called extroverts and the second introverts and it is possible to place a person on an extroversion-introversion scale, to put a number on him and compare him with others and with the norm or average. The scientific measurement is better than our often biased judgement because the scale is worked out over large samples and the tests are carried out carefully and systematically in a standardized way. You can get useful career advice by knowing such things. For instance, you will do better as a pub landlord or commercial traveller if you are well on the extroverted side but, if you want to be an accountant or draughtsman, you might do better if you were more introverted.

Another way in which we all vary from one another is in general intelligence. This is a very important way of being different. Most of us are around the average but we all know people who are a bit thick, slow on the uptake and enjoy simple, routine jobs. They are often the salt of the earth, kind, friendly and helpful but they have been short-changed upstairs.

Others – the clever-clogs and smart alecks – are too clever by half. With insincere tears of remorse I plead guilty to being one of that detested breed. Worse! I enjoy it and exploit it.

Extroversion, intelligence – we can measure them. And there are other ways of classifying people. But should we? Is it moral? Is it just? Is it in fact discrimination?

Why we have to judge each other and ourselves

Every age has its silly ideas and one of the silliest of our age is the laughably exaggerated attitude towards what is called 'discrimination'. It started with the enormous mixing of populations which was brought about by World War II. There was uninformed and unfair prejudice against incoming strangers who looked different and had a different skin colour, different life-styles and habits. And, learning better, many of us began to detest and condemn unfair, unwise and incorrect discrimination against these strangers who were trying to make their way among us. This was because the discrimination – or choice – was based on the wrong grounds: skin colour, appearance, manner of speech, religion, life-style – all details which have nothing to do with social merit or ability. It was misguided discrimination and it is rightly abhorred by decent people. In my experience in Mensa it is among the very intelligent that racial and cultural discrimination is at its minimum.

However, it subsequently became the fashion to declare that discrimination of any kind was harmful and evil. To favour good behaviour, to encourage excellence, to allow advanced education for the very clever child, to condemn parasites and criminals and to oppose disorder – all these have been castigated as discrimination by some extremists. Discrimination between right and wrong is condemned as just as wicked and shameful as the unfair discrimination described above.

A defence of discrimination

We are trying to live together in a co-operative society. This means that collectively we have to somehow sort ourselves out and if possible slot everyone into a suitable place in the system, where he or she can be comfortable and also make a contribution and a living. The idea that this can be done without discrimination is quite foolish. Imagine it. We need a new brain surgeon. We go to the unemployment register. Who has been out of work longest? Give him the tools. Start Monday. Next problem.

Let me be frank. If it comes to anyone doing anything with a scalpel to my own brain I make my position clear. I am in favour of the strictest and harshest discrimination against anyone who has not been subjected to rigorous selection, given privileged, elitist, specialist education and training, and labelled as a member of that most discriminating and exclusive elite, the Royal College of Surgeons.

This may seem a rather extreme example but surely it is true that we cannot sort ourselves out and slot ourselves in to the many different and highly specialist jobs that keep the whole system going without an awful lot of judging, testing, checking, choosing, selection, rejection, and (dread word!) discrimination going on all the time. And this need for careful selection and discrimination is becoming more urgent as our western industrial society becomes more complex. As new, more difficult jobs arise from advanced technology and as we automate away the undemanding jobs and the simpler skills we shall have to be more discriminating, not less so. The way the world is going we shall need to seek out and discriminate in favour of every clever person we can find. Then we must educate, train and suitably motivate the lot if we are to have a chance against world competition in the next millennium.

And this is the critical point. We have to do it and we want to do it as fairly as possible – and this means scientifically. If we use the scientific method it is about as far away from simple ignorant prejudice as we can get. Intelligence tests are blunt instruments, not very exact ones. But at least, within their limits, they are the fairest we know. They cannot see skin colour, religion, life-style or dreadlocks. Tests devised for one culture are less predictive on another but that can be overcome by 'culture fair' tests or tests for other cultures. I have used both kinds in this book. I do *not* claim that these tests are equally fair for all cultures. There is no such test. But there is nothing else with *less* unfairness. The race relations lobby is always telling those with white skins that they are all consciously or unconsciously racially biased, so we had better not trust human judgment. So, if we are not going to allocate positions by picking numbers from a hat, then we had better trust something.

Brains versus bombs

I have a prejudice in favour of brains. This will be clear as you read on. If you are prejudiced against intelligence and the brainy you might be wise to stop reading here. Otherwise bear with me while I try to justify my prejudice. I start with an admission. Brains can certainly solve human problems but they have a nasty way of creating new ones when they do so. However, the new problems are usually at a higher level, a result of the opening up of new roads, new possibilities for mankind and for all life. Brains applied to sanitation and medical knowledge have given us longer lives, so there are a lot more of us around. But longer lives and greater numbers of people create more problems. Long lives in fact have more problems than short ones. More people have more problems than fewer people. But I discriminate against the lesser problem load of fewer, shorter lives while I can. Most of us do.

The worst charge against brains is that, applied to fundamental physics, they have made the death of mankind possible. But I do not trust kind thoughts or peace pledges or goodness and simplicity to

11

reduce the risk. Brains have a way of solving the problems that brains create. And right now they are noticeably at work in the world of global politics trying hard to do just that. Brains, working anarchically in every direction all over the world, have created serious environmental problems but, again, I doubt whether they will be solved by goodwill, godliness, passion or prayers. It will be the clever clogs, the arguing, quarrelling, persistent scientists, technologists, engineers and industrialists who, using the best brains, instruments, education and training, will find the solution. It will be they who will have found out the facts and ascertained the trends. And it will be they, if anyone, who will worry, work and contrive a way out of the muddle we are in and into some unforeseen new muddle in the future. Life is like that. There will be no utopia.

Multiplying intelligence

What satisfies people soon changes. You probably live in one of the rich countries and most people are very much better off than elsewhere, at least in the goods, services, entertainments, sports, holidays, travel and health care that they can afford to enjoy and do enjoy. I have lived in poverty and in need through a couple of economic depressions and two very nasty wars.

Even the poorest today enjoy a better life-style than the majority did sixty years ago. Yet I cannot say that we are any happier or that we complain less. But none of us would choose to go back to those days. Those people all over the world who live now as we lived then would do anything to come and enjoy our standard of living rather than stay in their own countries. They would rather be relatively poor here than relatively rich in a less developed society.

So I am going to assume that complaining about the inadequacies of affluence is a better way to be than remaining patiently uncomplaining about real poverty and living in real discomfort with barely enough to eat.

It is of course galling to see the fat cats in Porsches when all we can afford is a second-hand Cortina, but no worse than being passed by that chap on the flashy Norton motor bike while cycling up a steep hill on a second-hand Raleigh with a wonky pedal.

If you agree that progress towards affluence is a good thing then I want to claim that we owe it, not so much to the brainy ones of this world, as to the fact that their talents have been used so well by the social system that has evolved. The pluralist, free-market western world, for all its many faults and injustices, has a way of making a very much better use of what brains and other skills there are around than any other system. In more primitive societies the brainy ones could influence a few people around them, could think up better ways of doing things, plan more effective activities for small communities and to some extent improve the life-style and efficiency of the people they were living with.

However, when the merchants and industrialists broke away from aristocratic control and established trading and manufacturing centres, mass-production factories came into existence. There was an amplification effect by which one really clever engineer could change the work methods of thousands, even millions of people. Fewer workers could create much more value and many times more goods and services for each man-year of work.

The great secret was that it was an evolutionary system. It discriminated well, it automatically chose success and excellence. There was no one big boss, no aristocrat, no government or politician picking people and deciding what was best, what we want or what we should have. It was decided by the competitive market. If something was better, easier to make and therefore cheaper it was chosen not by the bosses but by everyone. The unchosen variant faded away and the better product got the money it needed to expand and do more of the same. It was the self-selection of excellence. Good organizers tended to become the owners and managers of the factories and farms. Brains, ability, hard work – these were all automatically promoted.

Educated people with well-trained brains can reach the positions where they can do the most good. Everybody gets the benefit, not of the average intelligence but of the best intelligence. In these circumstances, with free competition and an open market, *and in no other conditions we have tried so far*, the cream rises to the top. A good brain is a social asset and not only to its possessor. It benefits the family, the community and the whole country as well.

Secret superbrains

Not all those that are blessed with a good brain are aware of it. I am not the only one to have been astonished to learn that what was different about me was in fact all right. Many of those who drew a winning ticket in the genetic lottery – a good, quick-thinking, efficient brain – think they are peculiar. They know they are different but think they are abnormal rather than supernormal. And some seek to hide their luck. This happens especially in humble families where there is no tradition of learning or education.

In these families the parents are often puzzled by a child who asks a million questions, thinks things out for him- or herself, greedily reads everything in sight and often out-thinks and out-talks the irritated parents. 'She is dead ignorant, always asking questions and never believes what she's told.' A really high-flying child can already possess an average adult mind as far as knowledge and understanding goes by the age of seven or eight. But emotionally he or she is still just a cheeky, lively, immature child. The family, friends, even the teachers, often want nice 'average' children, not those oddities who pester them with difficult questions they can't answer. It is hard for the parents and teachers of such little monsters.

Even in families which do have cultural and intellectual traditions the bright child can go unrecognized because the parents simply do not know what an outstanding child is like. 'He is a slow learner, nearly four and he can't read yet.' Every parent starts from scratch, not knowing what to expect.

And then there is the problem of the really secret superbrain. The child goes to primary school, is put into one of these wonderful, egalitarian 'mixed ability' classes, in which the poor teacher is struggling to deal with a dozen separate tables, each with a group ranging all the way from slow learners to our high-flyer with an IQ of 170 or so. A really bright child can have a mental age of 9 when he or she begins school at five years of age.

What happens? The clever child, like any other, is a conformist. Jane wants to be like the other kids. She wants to be liked – to be one of the gang. The poor little girl doesn't know what's 'wrong' with her. At first she answers questions readily until her sophistication and knowledge provoke puzzled looks and envious glances from the other children. And some teachers are none too patient with the confident, questioning little know-it-all who sometimes catches them out. Jane is a nuisance. She has read to the end of the set book on the first day of term and demands another and yet another. However, Jane soon gets the message. She sits quietly and goes off into daydreams because the pace of the class is too slow for her quick little brain. In this way Jane can waste three or four precious fast-learning years. Both she and the nation are the poorer for it.

Or there is Bobby. He went through that phase in a day or two. He can do all these simple sums and gets tired of the exciting information that 'the cat sat on the mat.' His restless curiosity leads him into other adventures in order to relieve the tedium. He discovers the weakness of many modern schools where the heads discourage 'discrimination' against mischief and indiscipline. He soon joins or forms the 'official opposition' whose main object in life is to provoke exciting distractions and make the teacher's life a misery.

Our secret superbrain's behaviour and cover up can take many forms. Some modern classroom fads and fashions are such that the secrets are never revealed. And some time in later life some adult is going to shrug and sigh, and regret what might have been.

The 'Equality' freaks

This age has been called the 'century of the common man.' Seen from that point of view it was preceded by a century of the uncommon man and it is the uncommon man (and woman) who seem to have made this rather prosperous century what it is. Not that the uncommon man has been absent or uninfluential in this century. But one gets the feeling that modern education, under the influence of certain political theories, is not doing much to keep up the supply.

The dream of a truly and completely equal society has made an enormous impact on our age in many parts of the world. Unrelenting attempts have been made to iron out the rich, beautiful and fruitful diversity of humanity and reduce all citizens to an accepted model, the official, inspected, approved and certified 'international standard person.' Wherever it has been really tried this equalization process has resulted in bloody, destructive and murderous tyranny and usually desperate poverty. The dream of human equality has cost millions of lives in the Soviet Union and eastern Europe, in Ethiopia, Cambodia, Viet Nam, China and many other places.

Other countries, led perhaps by the pioneers who set up the United States of America, had a different and much happier concept of equality, one which was compatible with, and not a denial of, freedom and personal liberty. These countries believed in equality before the law – equality of opportunity and equality of human rights. They believed in equality but not in uniformity. They recognized and rejoiced in the wonder and glory of human diversity. These are the principles of the western world, which is richer, more powerful and, since World War II at least, a lot more peaceable. There have been a lot of little wars since the last big one but nothing on the scale of what occurred in the past.

But despite all this the equality freaks are still around, claiming that we are all really clone-like equals and that we all deserve exactly equal provision, because any inequalities that emerge are not due to our differences in ability or effort but are the fault of 'the system' or the evil deeds of 'the ruling classes'.

Unfortunately these egalitarians are usually kindly and decent people who are blind to the horrors which their extremist ideas have brought when they have really been practised. Moreover, they are intoxicated by the beautiful simplicity of the idea that we are all created from one mould and that only bad luck or injustice creates the differences we see between us. They are even prepared to say that we are all born with exactly the same innate intelligence. From congenital idiot to genius, all difference is caused by inequalities of provision. This means that exactly the same education is suitable for all of us and that anything else would be wicked and unfair discrimination.

Now that would not be so bad if these egalitarians were just a cranky movement or a political party. But some of them have become teachers (often after an 'unfair' selective education) and the ideas they follow have, in many places, become widespread educational practice, which seems a pity. The result is that we, as a nation, are failing to find, suitably educate, train and motivate a lot of our best talents, especially those who come from humble backgrounds, as I did. And we are doing this in an age of high technology and fierce international competition, when it is most important that we should sort out and make the best possible use of our mental resources. So I am trying, in my humble way to find as many of the secret superbrains as I can and bring them to a realization of their potential. I do it for their own sake and for the general benefit.

By picking up the abandoned foundling, Mensa, when it was on the point of expiry and setting up an organization that grew from a hundred members to a hundred thousand I feel I have struck a small blow against the well-meaning but mistaken egalitarians. And I have helped the few million people who have taken the Mensa test or done the tests in my books to know themselves a little better. They have made the astonishing discovery that they are not all the same!

2

Measuring Human Differences

Measuring ability

'My Deare Adele, I am four years old, and I can read any English book. I can say all the Latin substantives, adjectives and active verbs, besides fifty two lines of Latin poetry. I can cast up any sum in addition and multiply by 2, 3, 4, 5, 6, 7, 8, 9, 10, 11. I read French a little and know the clock.' Francis Galton. 15th February 1827.

The tiny tot who wrote that was not lying about his age. Most people have no experience of such precociousness in a child. Indeed many are somewhat repelled by such forwardness. It seems 'unnatural'. But I can say from personal experience as the chairman of the Mensa Foundation for Gifted Children that there are a sprinkling of such brilliant children to be found everywhere. It is chance, luck. One in a thousand, one in ten thousand wins a big prize in the genetic lottery. They are to be found in all areas, minorities and classes. One of my grand-daughters was reading a score of words well before she was two years old and I know a boy aged four and a half who writes pages of good English prose on a word processor on his own. In the Mensa Foundation we are finding them every day.

Sir Francis Galton fulfilled his early promise. The tiny tot grown up was a genius and one of the first who conducted a thorough and scientific enquiry into genius in man. Among his close relatives were some of the intellectual giants of Victorian times – Erasmus Darwin and Charles Darwin amongst others. In 1869 Sir Francis Galton published his book *Hereditary Genius*, which started a new trend in thinking. It is claimed that he was the first to think about human cognitive or intellectual ability in a systematic and scientific way and

17

that he is the real founder of psychology. He treated the subject of human talent in a statistical manner so as to arrive at predictable numerical results.

Galton achieved much in his laboratory at King's College, London, in the measurement of other human dimensions such as height, weight, length and width of skull, and found that there were strange regularities about them when looked at in the mass. The measurements, plotted against the number who had them, fall, he ascertained, on the bell-shaped curve discovered by Friedrich Gauss and illustrated below.

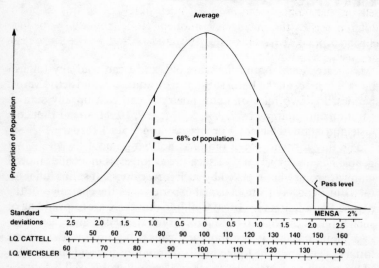

THE NORMAL CURVE

No matter what measurement he took he always found the same thing. The closer a measurement is to the average for that measurement, the more people there are that have that measurement. As you get further from the average the people who have it get rarer and rarer. There are masses of men clustering around the middle height (175 cm in Britain) but only a scattering of 120 cm dwarfs and 200 cm giants. Galton was the first to spot that the same thing applied, with differences, in human intelligence. He examined the records of a thousand famous people who could be assumed to be highly intelligent – judges, generals, scientists, statesmen, etc. He came to the conclusion, that the blood relatives of such people were nearly 130 times more likely than the average to be distinguished and evidently highly intelligent. What Galton discovered that is of importance today is that the idea of the 'international standard person' is a dangerous myth and that there are enormous differences, which can be seen from early childhood, in the ability of people to use their brains.

The Gaussian bell curve demonstrates the way living things vary from the average. Any variable (way of being different) on a living system which fits on this curve is said to have a 'normal distribution'. The distance from the centre (the summit of the curve) across the graph tells us the difference from the average. The height of the curve tells us the number who *are* that much different. In this case the difference is in the intelligence quotient (IQ). Notice how people cluster around the average IQ (100) and tail off as the score gets greater or lesser.

The need to know

Even if there are such differences we can ask 'So What? Do we really need to know?'

Well, before Galton's time no one had even thought of trying to measure anything as subtle and tricky as our ability to use our brains to solve problems and understand things. We managed without mental tests for millions of years, why should we need them now? Well, we managed without thermometers too and relied on feel to judge the temperature. But we do find thermometers useful when we become ill.

But there is a much more important reason why there is a real need to know, especially today when so much of the education system is geared to the average and below-average child. The many towering geniuses of the Victorian age created the conditions for the industrial society which has made life in much of the world longer, healthier, richer, safer and more pleasant. Before those days we had plenty of brainy people to supply the few clerks, lawyers, priests and doctors who were needed. Most of the population was slaving away on the land in order to extract a meagre living, a small space under a roof, a limited range of food apart from the staple, bread, a few sticks of furniture and some pots and pans. There was much demand for strong muscles and little demand for brains. (A lot of places are still like that today.)

19

Nowadays it is not muscular workers who create the wealth, but the vast amount of cleverly designed capital equipment and machinery. Ingenious robots and automats work in farms and factories. Some 90% of us used to work on the land in order to scratch a bare living. Now 5% of us work and maintain the tricky, complicated machines that produce enormous surpluses. Butter mountains, wine lakes and meat hills are created by complex farm machinery, run by highly educated and technologically trained agriculturalists.

The countryman of the past was seen as a yokel, none too clever, who knew how to wield a sickle. Not any more. We may not like it but we had better face up to it. There is not so much work any more for the slow thinker, or even the average thinker. We are all much more dependent upon the small proportion of very clever ones at that upper tail (on the right-hand side) of Gauss's normal distribution curve. We shall not be able to waste our best talents any more. For all our sakes we shall have to seek them out as early as we can and make sure we make the best use of them. That means education and training – special education, special training, selectively suitable education and training – not just the 'British standard kite-marked teaching courses for the British standard kite-marked child'. Even Karl Marx wanted 'from each according to his ability'. And the able can do much more for us all now than they did then.

Educational selection

The significance of all that I have said above is this. A nation that depends for its living on high technology and industrial and commercial excellence has special problems as regards education. It has to be certain that every child capable of learning it, knows enough arithmetic and can read and write, at least, our common language, English. Each normal child should also know some basic science, history, geography and something about the laws and traditions of the land it is to live in. According to many accounts we still have a fair way to go before we achieve even this modest aim. In fact, the National Curriculum has had to be introduced in order to take care of this obvious need.

However, once we abandon the idea of standard education for the standard child, once we accept the very great differences between children in their educability – the capacity to absorb and benefit from education – we shall be forced to admit that the education and training of the very educable is, strictly from the national point of view, much more important than the further education of those who are average and below average in their ability to benefit. More money spent on the early identification, selection, and specialist education of the high-fliers can do more for the nation than more money spent, for instance, on raising the school age of below-average children, who often benefit little from the last few years of education anyway. It is the teachers who tell me this. Many decent but slow-learning children spend the last three years bored to death, truanting, playing up and learning little, when they are longing to be released from educational conscription so that they can find work and learn a job. These are facts not recommendations.

There is a law of diminishing returns in education which goes something like this. The more intelligent and studious a child is, the more time, effort and resources can be spent upon its education before we reach the limit of what the child needs and wants, and from which the child and the nation can benefit. At the level of higher education this excellent principle is already recognized and we do, sensibly enough, have a selective system for polytechnics, universities, medical schools and so on.

The next point arises from elementary psychological theory. Between birth and five years nearly all children learn how to use their enormously complex muscular system, to see and hear, to learn and recognize things and people, and to speak a language quite well – several languages if they are exposed to them. Of course they learn a lot after that but the basics, the really difficult learning upon which all the rest is to be built up, all happen in the first few years. The rule is simple: the younger you are the faster you learn.

Thus the present non-selective system at pre-school (nursery), primary and secondary level in state education, creates an enormous waste of talent. Selection and specialist education for high-flyers, very studious and intelligent children, are not provided by most local education authorities. But it is at the nursery, primary and secondary level that the learning ability of every child, clever or not, is at its greatest. It is at these ages that the failure to stimulate and motivate the really able child has the worst effect. From the point of view of simply acquiring the most education, of raising the most children to the highest level, we can say this. Money and effort spent at the nursery school level can do most good. Resources allocated at the primary level come next, and then secondary level, higher education coming last in importance in the education of the whole community. Today we spend a very large slice of our national budget on education and we do it in a way that is exactly upside-down.

It is quite possible to spot the promising child, the very educable child, before school age. There ought to be many more special schools where such children could spend part of their time, at least, with teachers who have learnt by experience how to deal with the fast learner. Such a child, languishing in the maintained sector of education, is just a curious and somewhat frightening exception, a nuisance and a trouble to a teacher who must necessarily have been trained to cope with normal, average children. The high-flyers should mix with their peers for play, worship, meals, sports and games, but for lessons they need – and we all need them to have – teachers who can cope with them. Yes, we have to 'cream them off'. There is nothing wrong with educational cream. What is scorned as elitist is plain common sense. We cannot run an advanced technological society on homogenized educational milk. There is no way of recognizing and developing excellence without 'labelling' it.

Science and measurement

So we come to the big controversial question. Several times a year some journalist or politician rediscovers that intelligence tests have been proved to be 'meaningless', or else they are 'biased against the minorities' (actually some 'minorities' do quite well in them, better than average.) Yes, and 'all they measure is the ability to do intelligence tests.'

What it all amounts to is that some people absolutely detest the idea that intelligence is just another way of being different, like being short or fair-haired. We all, including those who condemn IQ tests, make daily judgments about those we work with, know and meet. We think and we say that this individual is cunning, that one is thick, John is bright, Jack is a good old plodder but slow on the uptake, Sheila is nothing to look at but a bit of a wit, while Joan is lovely but what a scatterbrain!

Now these differences are manifest and, basing ourselves upon them, we all make judgments and decisions, hire and fire, marry and befriend, and promote and sack. It is, therefore, hard to believe that there is no way to standardize them over large samples and draw more reliable conclusions which are statistically verifiable.

Casually looking at people and listening to them once or twice or listening to gossip about them, we can make decisions that affect our life and theirs. Why should we not do so after a careful examination based on much scrupulously validated research?

Statistical methods

'Hard' science is based on the general idea that the elements of the system are always the same, invariable. One proton is just like another. One hydrogen atom is indistinguishable from any other hydrogen atom. One batch of sulphur or gold or carbon dioxide behaves the same as any other batch. But living things, men and women among them, are just not like that. Every single one is unique. They are all different from one other in many ways, and any science applied to them must take account of the many ways of being different.

Accordingly, the early 'soft' scientists, the biological scientists such as Galton, had to work out a sort of mathematics to deal with entities, with things which, unlike atoms and molecules, differ from some norm or average. What they found was that there were general things you *could* say about whole groups which were useful and predictive. There were loose, on-the-average laws relating to the spread and concentration of qualities in living species. They did not deal in certainties but in probabilities. It is best to know how *likely* some things are to happen if there is no way of knowing *for sure* that they will happen, as we do with the rising and setting of the sun and the moon. These were the methods that led to the systematic basis for a method for measuring intelligence.

Professor Arthur Binet in Paris was asked to deal with a problem when it was decided that all children, not just the rich ones and the clever ones who could win scholarships, were going to have to go to school. There were a few children who seemed very slow and almost unteachable and the authorities wanted to identify them as early as possible, so as to get them taught by specialist teachers and not hold back all the rest of the class.

Binet established the concept of a mental age. A child with a *mental age* of ten was any child of any age who could do all the things that an *average* ten-year-old could do and no more. Binet arranged a questionnaire, a little examination which every child could take. This test was designed so that no child could answer all the questions in the time allowed, but the questions became progressively more difficult, so that he could find the point on the scale which the average seven-year-old, eight-year-old, nine-year-old and ten-year-old, could reach. Thus he could establish the mental age of any child. Then he compared the mental age with the actual age of the child, simply by dividing the mental age by the true age. This gave a number which expressed the backwardness or forwardness of the child. It would be about 0.5 in the case of a very backward child, going up to 1.7 or 1.8 for a very forward child. Later Professor Terman simplified the idea by multiplying the result by 100 so as to get rid of the decimals. So the dull child would be said to have an IQ or intelligence quotient of 50 and the very bright ones an IQ of 170 or 180.

The work of Binet had an enormous influence and the idea was taken up by psychologists all over the world. It provided a simple, straightforward and fair way in which the teachability – the ability to understand and learn – could be estimated, regardless of the level of the child's education. What a well-designed intelligence test does is to find out, not what you know, in the manner of a normal examination, but how well and easily you can learn and understand what you learn.

Ability unfairly shared

Three unexpected things came from the great flood of research in many lands which followed the work of Binet. Spearman verified what many teachers had already noticed: the children who were very forward in one subject tended to be forward in all the others as well. There is a 'to them that hath shall be given' trend in the distribution of thinking power. It seems unfair. It might be nicer if those who were good at one thing were less likely to good at others. However, that is not the way nature has arranged matters. Of course I am talking about a biological tendency not a law, so if you happen to know a child who is marvellous at arithmetic and poor at French, it does not disprove the case, which is supported by thorough research in many places.

The intelligence ceiling

The other odd thing the researchers found is that mental age stops advancing somewhere between 14 and 18 years (the brighter you are the older). In fact, it even drops a little as you grow older. So when it comes to measuring an adult IQ we have to stop the calendar on actual age at 14. It is a rather peculiar system but it works out all right as long as you understand it. I myself prefer not to talk about IQ but about a more useful figure that you can obtain from knowing the IQ and the standard deviation (the spread of scores) of the test concerned. In Mensa we go by the percentile, which simply tells what percentage of the general population would score less than you do. If you are on the 50 percentile you score better than 50% – you are in fact completely average. On the 98 percentile you are pretty bright, bright enough to join Mensa because you score as well as, or better than, 98% of the population.

Intelligence is fairly constant

The third fact that arose from this early research is the most important. What Binet, Spearman, Terman, Cattell, Pearson, Burt, Wechsler and the other pioneers found was that, by and large, over large samples the intelligence quotient remains fairly constant as a child grows older. If a child has a mental age of ten at the age of five, it will usually have a mental age of fourteen when it reaches seven and so on.

Are IQ tests bogus?

The reader will have read a number of criticisms of IQ testing, so I had better tackle them. The first thing to be said is that most of the really destructive criticism come from people who are not psychologists and who show by their writings that they have become obsessively attached to an egalitarian political dogma.

One of the most severe critics, Professor Kamin, has managed to persuade himself that psychometricians all over the world who use intelligence tests are doing it so as to oppress the poor.

There are fair criticisms of IQ tests of course. They are far from perfect. The most serious criticism is that most of the currently used tests were devised early in the century and very few have been updated and revised and re-standardized as they should have been. Several generations of psychologists have concentrated on criticizing the work of the pioneers rather than on the difficult job of developing and improving their work.

Unfair to minorities?

For instance, many psychologists complain about the cultural bias of standard tests when used on minority groups instead of devising tests which *are* standardized on those groups and, therefore, *are* fair for them. It goes without saying that all those different groups which we distinguish because of some very noticeable difference such as skin colour, the so-called 'ethnic' or ethnic minority groups have, all of them, the full range of every other kind of difference including intelligence. There are black, brown, white and yellow high-flyers and the same range of pigmentation in low-flyers. Skin colour is what we call an independent variable. It has a low correlation, if any, with brains. If you want to find clever people use an IQ test not a colour matching sample test.

The truth is of course that the group tested has to have a way of understanding the test, a background of common experience. Different groups have different languages and cultures, and the standardization and marking of the test ought to be done on the group originally tested. If the test was based on a fair sample of white schoolchildren in England in 1930 it will be not be quite so valid on, say, a group of English-speaking Asians in England in 1990. However, we cannot say that it is 'unfair' to the Asians because, if it were, we would expect them to score worse than the white children, whereas in fact they score better. On the whole we can say that the effect of cultural bias tends to be exaggerated and that the more intelligent a child is the less it matters. Of course, no one can be tested in a language they do not understand. However, our experience in Mensa is that many foreigners whose knowledge of English is by no means great do surprisingly well in English language tests.

There is such a thing as a 'culture free' or 'culture fair' test which does not include language items. It consists entirely of diagrams with a few very simple instructions. The strange thing is that people from some minority cultures tend to do rather worse in these than in the English language tests. There is an example of such a test later in this book. I do not see how any one can really claim that these are 'easier' for people of one race or culture than another, providing they have all been exposed to schooling. (Obviously a New Guinea tribesman would not know what a diagram was. It would not be a test for him.)

In general, we can say that any test will tend to show up very bright children or adults, but the lower the IQ of the individual the more important it is to set a test that is fair to the minorities.

We must always bear in mind what I said above: that the IQ test is less unfair than any other test or judgment that can be made. It is the best we can do at the moment. You do not throw away a lifebelt because it is not a lifeboat. The IQ test has a great reputation for being able to probe below the surface of cultural disadvantage and spot the real potential underneath. If 43 years of testing millions of people for Mensa has proved anything it has proved that.

There is another point about the 'unfair to minorities' claim which seems important. Those who advance this argument are usually the same people who claim that differences of intelligence arise from cultural differences – different kinds of upbringing.

Now if people emigrate, if they move from one culture to another, whatever they do and wherever they go they will be under a disadvantage. They will find that all the examinations, assessments, methods of selection etc., will be adapted to and suitable for the host culture they have moved into, not the one they came from. The methods used will have evolved to help *that* society sort itself out and get the right people into the right positions. If an English industrial worker migrated to a preindustrial agricultural community he would find that he was completely lost and that the means used to pick good farmers or hut makers or potters would not select him. If he wanted to progress and do well he would need to learn how to qualify against the criteria which counted in the culture he had joined. It would do him no good to talk about his four 'A' levels, nor would he be wise to insist on introducing an A-level examination into the local culture to correct his 'unfair disadvantage'. The sensible people among the immigrant minorities have taken this point and many of them are doing better, on average, at our kind of test (and this includes intelligence tests) than the normal British child.

I believe that intelligence tests do evaluate real differences that apply to people from all cultures. But, even if I am wrong, they certainly are a way of finding out early which children are capable of absorbing the sort of higher education that you get in an advanced industrial society. There is no reason for changing them or rejecting them because that is the sort of society we live in. Our immigrant friends and colleagues seem to have preferred it. They accept its methods of selection and sensibly concentrate on equalling and beating the natives at their own game.

The practice effect

A criticism about the tests which is partially valid is that there is a 'practice effect'. If you do a number of intelligence tests you might get a slightly higher score on the next one. The effect is, on the average, about six IQ points. The theory of the test is that every candidate comes to it fresh and any practice will lead to a chance of over-estimation. If you want to avoid self-deception you should deduct a few points if you have had a lot of practice.

They only measure the ability to do tests

This sounds very clever but it is nonsense. The scores on tests are very predictive. Psychiatrists cannot do without them. Many companies use them for personnel selection; the armed forces in many countries use them with excellent results. They predict academic success more accurately than any other tests and they have been extensively validated by teachers' judgment, examination results and career success, and in many other ways.

How do you test people who are brighter than you are?

The answer is speed. The bright are quick-thinking. Most tests are timed. They have to be arranged so that only the very cleverest can finish the last item. If you complete the test with time to spare and make no mistakes, you have reached the test ceiling.

I had an awful cold

We are often asked by disappointed candidates whether the fact that they had a cold, or were menstruating, or had a bilious attack would make any difference to the score. Of course it is not a good idea to take a test when you do not feel up to it, but research shows that these factors have little, if any, effect.

Counter-criticism

Let me take to the offensive. I was brought up in working-class surroundings in the 1920s and 1930s and, as I have said, I was 'discovered' and revised my ambitions and self-concept only after an intelligence test given by the army in 1945.

I believe that the long-term, persistent denigration of IQ testing by an intellectual elite of university-educated people has been extremely detrimental to millions of able children from humble homes, and worse – to the nation itself. It has condemned enormous numbers of bright, teachable children to being undereducated in unsuitable schools by teachers who have no chance to get to grips with their very different problems.

I do not doubt the sincerity of this influential elite in trying to persuade us that testing intelligence is ineffective, unfair and evil. I believe they really thought that doing away with grammar schools, and eventually all private schools, would improve things for the working class. I am sure they have been disastrously mistaken. What they have achieved is exactly the opposite to what they intended.

If you want your brains tested I invite you to go on to the next five chapters.

3

About the Tests

Guesstimate testing

I will not deceive you. To develop, standardize and validate an intelligence test is a very long and expensive task which will cost hundreds of thousand of pounds if it is to be done properly. You have to find a very large random sample of people of all ages and do an enormous amount of calculating and checking. Then you can supply the test only to qualified psychologists, who take great pains to keep the test and the answers confidential. If you went to an educational psychologist for such a test it would cost you about £150 a time.

No one would dream of allowing such a test to be published for the general public to see. If the test were published in a book like this it would be goodbye to all the work and money you had spent to develop and standardize it. The test would be useless because the answers would have been published. So what I am offering here are guesstimate tests which can give you a fair idea of what your score would be on a proper test supervised by an expert. I developed the tests by looking at others which are out of circulation but had been properly standardized in the past. I devised closely similar questions which use the same principles and the same sort of 'distracters' (things to make the problem difficult). I have done a lot of them at various times in my different books and they have proved to be a good first approximation tested on Mensa groups and other helpers.

Testing different groups

I give two English-language tests which are reasonably valid for people who are really familiar with English and can read and write. For other groups they are less valid but can, nevertheless, give some indication. I also include an example of a culture fair test. This consists entirely of diagrams and will give you an idea no matter what language your mother tongue is. Anyone who has any familiarity with diagrams at all could do this without serious disadvantage. The negative side is that the kind of intelligence evaluated by this sort of test is somewhat different from the verbal intelligence tested by the written tests. Such graphic tests are slightly biased in favour of those who are good at understanding space relationships and mathematics and against those with language and understanding skills. These two abilities correlate very well in most people, but there are some who make up for a loss in one area by extra ability in the other. The difference should not be great for most people, but you have both kinds of test, so you will be able to tell which way you are if you do much better in one than in the other. In working out the results it is wise to take the average score on all tests as the closest approximation. It is all right to cheat on time or by looking things up. You will be deceiving no one but yourself. However, if you really want to know it is best to stick to the rules.

How you learn and what you learn

The tests are designed to evaluate how well you can think rather than what you know. I try to use very familiar words, so that you are looking for subtle shades of meaning or unfamiliar relationships among the words. All the tests start with simple ideas and get more difficult as they go along. There are no catches. In the advanced culture fair test I have assumed that no one under average intelligence is likely to try the test. Accordingly, I have not included many questions for the lower mental ages.

Good results, bad results

I have to say this. Neither very good results in these tests nor very bad ones should be taken too seriously. You can put more trust in good results than bad ones, however. It is very rare for anyone to get an outstanding score which is not reliable. But retesting low scorers more often brings surprises. If you do not know your intelligence the test will give you a better idea of where you stand. In the chapter on Mensa I explain how you can get a really valid test carried out.

THE TESTS

General explanation and instructions

A heckler at one of my lectures noisily informed the meeting that people who read my books want their brains tested. I could not deny it, they do. I will be frank and admit my belief that the reason you, my dear reader, picked up this book was because that is just what you want. So here we go.

Millions of people have turned to Mensa for just that service. I shall start by being frank with you. Few professional psychologists would admit that there is much merit in a self-administered test like those in this book.

If you take the tests given here seriously and time yourself properly you will be able to know yourself a little better than you do now. And if you do well on them I hope you will consider joining me as another of 100,000 colleagues in the worldwide high-IQ society, Mensa. I can honestly recommend it.

So here is an effort, as good as you are likely to get in any generally published book, to give you a chance to accept the challenge and amuse yourself finding out whether you are really bright or whether you just think you are.

I have explained the problems about intelligence testing and the reasonable and unreasonable criticisms it faces. Tests cannot be valid for every subculture in a large country with diverse communities like Britain and we have no practical way of making allowances for people from *any* different culture. However, verbal skill, the ability to understand written or spoken words, is the best indicator of intelligence there is. And I include a culture fair test that requires only enough English to read simple instructions.

The first two are language and number tests and they are fairly good indicators for those who are really familiar with written English. This is an English book and both the book and these tests are designed for people who read English fluently.

The culture fair test has no language items. This is to help the people in cases in which English is not their native language. As I have said, diagram tests measure a slightly different sort of intelligence, one which correlates highly with verbal intelligence but which is more associated with ability to understand and visualize spatial relationships. Mathematicians usually do well in culture fair tests. Professor Raymond Cattell believes that they detect what he calls 'fluid' intelligence, that is, the basic inborn intelligence rather than what he describes as 'crystallized' intelligence. In crystallized intelligence the differences between people are more affected, he says, by what they have learnt and how they use their native intelligence. It will be interesting to compare your results on the three tests. The best guesstimate of all would be to add your IQ results from all three and divide by three.

General instructions

These are timed tests and it is essential to keep to the timetable if the result is to be meaningful. It is a good idea to get someone to time you or to set an alarm clock and put your pencil firmly down when it says 'time is up'.

You need a scrap pad, a pencil or two, sharpened at both ends, and a quiet desk in a warm comfortable room at a time when you can rely on an hour without interruption for each of the first two tests and about a quarter of an hour for the third. (Several sessions, one for each test, is OK.) Put your answering machine on or take the phone off the hook. It is also OK to 'stop the clock' for unexpected interruptions you cannot avoid.

Work as quickly and as thoroughly as you can. There are no catch questions. It is all right to guess if you do not know for sure; there is no penalty for errors. If a question calls for two answers it is an error if you do not give both. There are no half marks.

If you give more answers to a question than are called for you get no marks, even if the right answer is given. It is all right to alter an answer before your time is up, but you must indicate your final choice clearly and use it to assess your score.

4

Test A

Word and number intelligence test (English)

YOU HAVE ONE HOUR. START YOUR TIMING NOW, READ THE INSTRUCTIONS AND START THE TEST.

Directions
Start at the beginning and go straight through. Never mind if the questions seem easy at first. Do them all as carefully and as quickly as you can. They get harder later. Stop after one hour exactly. Do not spend too much time on questions you cannot answer.

START HERE

Read these words

  potato carrot swede <u>apple</u> turnip

'apple' is underlined because it is the 'odd one out'. They are all root vegetables except apple, which is a fruit.

Now underline the odd one out in these lists.

  1. dog cat mouse house sheep
  2. cabbage potato mint lettuce parsley
  3. valley hill gorge canyon vale
  4. second century metre hour week
  5. sit crawl kneel stand lie
  6. brooch ring necklace scarf earring

Look at these numbers

2 4 . . . . 8 10

What is the missing number? It is 6 because the numbers are increasing by two at each step. Fill in the 6.

How about this?

1 2 4 . . . . 16 32 64. What number is missing here? It is 8 because they double at each step.

Now fill in the gap in each line below:

7. 10 12 14 . . . . 18 20 22
8. 30 27 24 . . . . 18 15 12
9. 3 7 11 . . . . 19 23 27
10. 18 16 14 12 . . . . 12 14 16 18
11. 3 4 6 7 . . . . 10 12 13 15
12. 4 6 9 13 . . . . 24 31 39 48

Here is a list of numbered words

1	humid	6	large	11	quiet
2	tender	7	push	12	big
3	rapid	8	wide	13	keen
4	lose	9	idle	14	pale
5	right	10	clumsy	15	tense

Example 1: 'narrow' means the OPPOSITE of 'wide', which is word number 8.
Example 2: 'inactive' means the SAME as 'idle', which is word number 9.

Put the number of the correct word in the above list in the spaces provided (dotted lines) in the list below.

13. 'slow' means the OPPOSITE of word No. . . . . .
14. 'broad' means the SAME as word No. . . . . .
15. 'energetic' means the OPPOSITE of word No. . . . . .
16. 'big' means the SAME as word No. . . . . .
17. 'pull' means the OPPOSITE of word No. . . . . .
18. 'wet' means the SAME as word No. . . . . .
19. 'win' means the OPPOSITE of word No. . . . . .
20. 'tough' means the OPPOSITE of word No. . . . . .

21. 'noisy' means the OPPOSITE of word No. . . . .
22. 'sharp' means the SAME as word No. . . . .
23. 'skilful' means the OPPOSITE of word No. . . . .
24. 'wrong' means the OPPOSITE of word No. . . . .
25. 'fraught' means the SAME as word No. . . . .
26. 'dark' means the OPPOSITE of word No. . . . .
27. 'large' means the SAME as word No. . . . .
28. 'awkward' means the SAME as word No. . . . .

Look at these words
cloth table (jug jar <u>saucer</u> plate dish <u>cup</u>)
A cloth goes on a table and a cup goes on a saucer so we underline
'cup' and 'saucer'.
In the questions below you have to underline the two words in the
brackets which connect the same way as the first two words.

29. pine tree (pip fruit juice apple nut core)
30. cut bread (file saw smack wood cake scoop)
31. man husband (baby woman child friend wife aunt)
32. eyes see (skin ears nose arms lips hear listen)
33. wicked good (bad calm kind sad friendly cruel)
34. think dream (drowsy scheme awake day asleep time)
35. plus minus (green blue red grey black white)
36. gas air (stone earth liquid methane milk butter)

Here are some letters arranged in a square. Notice the arrangement. E
is just after W, U is just below W, D is between S and F.

Q   W   E   R   T

Y   U   I   O   P

A   S   D   F   G

H   J   K   L   Z

Now answer these questions
37. Which letter is just above the letter before D?
38. Which letter is just before the letter just above J?
39. Which letter is halfway between A and G?

40. Which letter is between the letter just above S and the letter just below R?

41. Which letter is just above the letter that comes just before the letter that is just below D?

42. Which letter is between the letter which is between U and O and the letter between J and L?

43. Which letter is just before the letter just above the letter which is between J and L?

44. Which letter is just after the letter that is just above the letter just before the letter just above D?

45. Which letter is just above the letter which is just after the letter which is just between the letter just above L and just below O?

46. Which letter is between the letter which is just above the letter which is just after the letter just below the letter A, and the letter just below the letter just before the letter just above the letter G?

In each of these lines TWO of the words do not fit in with the other four. Underline the TWO words in each case.

47. wine   soda-water   potatoes   buns   beer   lemonade
48. stand   walk   lie   listen   rest   sit
49. rudeness   gratitude   envy   idiocy   hatred   unkindness
50. good-natured   short   kindly   fierce   gentle   friendly
51. tomorrow   instantly   here   where   far   close

Fill in the spaces in the lines below.

52. 1   4   9   25 49
53. 0   4   10 28   40   54
54. 60   58   55 50   48   45
55. 4   7   13 49   97   193
56. 4   6   5 6   8   7
57. 100   81   64 36   25   16

Here is a another list of numbered words

1	courage	6	scatter	11	conflict
2	evade	7	affix	12	satisfied
3	help	8	enormous	13	leave
4	increase	9	distorted	14	hasten
5	accept	10	pride	15	smash

Put the number of the correct word from the above list where the dotted lines are in the list below.

58. 'seek' means the OPPOSITE of word No. . . . .
59. 'cowardice' means the OPPOSITE of word No. . . . .
60. 'receive' means the SAME as word No. . . . .
61. 'decrease' means the OPPOSITE of word No. . . . .
62. 'gather' means the OPPOSITE of word No. . . . .
63. 'aid' means the SAME as word No. . . . .
64. 'minuscule' means the OPPOSITE of word No. . . . .
65. 'attach' means the SAME as word No. . . . .
66. 'shame' means the OPPOSITE of word No. . . . .
67. 'misshappen' means the SAME as word No. . . . .
68. 'accord' means the OPPOSITE of word No. . . . .
69. 'content' means the SAME as word No. . . . .
70. 'depart' means the SAME as word No. . . . .
71. 'mend' means the OPPOSITE of word No. . . . .
72. 'hurry' means the SAME as word No. . . . .
73. 'disperse' means the SAME as word No. . . . .

In the lines below you have to underline the two words in the brackets which connect the same way as the first two words.

74. anger insult (hatred rage compliment defiance temper pleasure)
75. land lake (hill valley sea plain island gulf)
76. painting eye (sound noise ear nose song shout)
77. present future (past what when then now how)
78. agree quarrel (fight attack peace submit war concur)
79. may must (permissible possible impossible imperative doubtful probable)
80. satellite Earth (Earth Sun star galaxy Venus meteor)
81. kilometre millimetre (metre century kilogram second amp pint)

A vat holds 200 litres of liquid. With the inflow valve open the liquid enters at the rate of 40 litres a minute. When the outflow valve is open the liquid drains away at 60 litres a minute. Bearing those figures in mind answer the following questions.

82. The vat is empty, the inflow valve is open and the outflow valve closed. How many minutes will it take to fill the vat?

83. The vat is full and both valves are open. How many minutes to empty the tank?

84. The vat is empty and the outflow valve is closed. The inflow valve is turned on for three minutes then closed as the outflow valve is opened. How many minutes does it take to empty the vat?

85. The vat is full with both valves open. After 4 minutes the inflow valve is closed. How many minutes from that time does it take to empty the vat?

86. The vat is full. The outflow valve is opened. 2 minutes later the inflow valve is opened with the outflow valve still open. How many litres will there be in the tank at the end of 3 minutes?

87. The outflow valve is closed and the tank is empty. The inflow is turned on for 4 minutes. The outflow is now opened with the inflow still on. How many litres will there be in the vat after 6 minutes?

THAT IS THE END OF TEST A. IF YOU HAVE SOME TIME LEFT CONTINUE TO CHECK YOUR ANSWERS UNTIL YOUR TIME IS UP. The answers and the method of scoring are given on pages 69–70. The next test is Test B, the word, number and graphics intelligence test (English). It begins in the following chapter.

5

Test B

Word, number and graphics intelligence test (English)

YOU HAVE ONE HOUR. START YOUR TIMING NOW, READ THE INSTRUCTIONS AND START THE TEST.

Directions

Answer the questions as quickly and carefully as you can. Begin at the beginning and go straight through. The questions are easy at first, but become progressively harder. Answer them carefully. There are no catches. Do not spend too much time on a question you cannot answer.

START HERE

Study these words

oval, square, round, <u>shape</u>, oblong

Four of the words are descriptive forms therefore 'shape' is underlined. Now study the following words:

<u>fish</u>, eel, salmon, herring, plaice

The word 'fish' is underlined as the others are names of fish.

In the lines below underline the word which tells you what type of things are named by the other words.

1. marrow, bean, cabbage, vegetable, leek
2. red, colour, green, blue, yellow
3. dog, cat, moose, animal, bull
4. material, satin, silk, denim, gingham
5. table, chair, settee, bed, furniture
6. game, football, hockey, netball, rugby
7. salt, mustard, condiment, pepper, vinegar
8. paper, label, stationery, envelope, notebook
9. elm, oak, ash, willow, tree
10. instrument, clarinet, trombone, trumpet, guitar
11. slippers, boots, shoes, footwear, clogs
12. Kent, County, Lincolnshire, Berkshire, Dorset
13. whale, dolphin, mammal, lion, tiger

Study these words

fat, slim, obese, thin, red

'fat' and 'obese' mean the same and 'thin' has the opposite meaning, so these three words are underlined.

In the lines below find the two words which mean the same, or almost the same, and a word which means the opposite. Underline these three words.

14. small, round, large, select, little
15. blessed, unhappy, sad, stated, pleased
16. high, low, warble, tall, unsteady
17. colourful, ugly, pretty, awkward, plain
18. flat, course, level, oddity, uneven
19. dull, shiny, paint, dingy, polish
20. reign, foreign, native, strange, mediocre
21. petty, unusual, important, likely, trivial

Look at these numbers

3, 5, 7, 9, 11, (13), (15)

You will notice that 13 and 15 are written in the brackets as they continue the correct sequence.

Here is another example

64, 32, 16, 8, (4), (2)

As you can see, 4 and 2 follow in the correct sequence.

Do the same with the following sequences, putting in the brackets the two numbers which you think follow correctly.

22. 6, 10, 14, 18, 22, ( ), ( )
23. 9, 12, 16, 21, 27, ( ), ( )
24. 54, 51, 49, 46, 44, 41, ( ), ( )
25. 7, 13, 19, 25, 31, ( ), ( )
26. 5, 24, 8, 22, 11, 20, 14, 18, ( ), ( )

Look at these

one penny, one pound, twopence, three pounds, fifty pence

If put in the correct order from smallest to largest they would be:

one penny, twopence, <u>fifty pence</u>, one pound, three pounds

'fifty pence' comes in the middle so is underlined.

In the lines below find the word or number which should be in the middle. Underline it.

27. 0   −1   10   20   −7
28. planet, sun, galaxy, universe, meteor
29. hotel, hut, house, castle, skyscraper
30. Pacific, Indian, Atlantic, Arctic, Mediterranean

Look at these rows of numbers

9, 4, 16, 6, 37, 23
10, 5, 17, 7, 38, 24

Each number in the lower row is one more than the one above it.

Now look at these

30, 14, 18, 22, 66
15, . ., . ., 11, 33

Each number in the lower row is half the number above it. Two numbers have been missed out. They are 7 and 9. Look at the following sequences, note the relationship between the two rows of numbers and fill in the missing ones.

31.	6,	19,	4,	8,	17,	14,	10,	16
	5,	18,	3,	7,	16,	. .,	. .,	15
32.	42,	18,	9,	81,	27,	54,	63,	60
	14,	6,	3,	27,	9,	. .,	. .,	20
33.	13,	3,	7,	21,	61,	9,	11,	50
	28,	8,	16,	44,	124,	. .,	. .,	102
34.	18,	24,	36,	72,	16,	50,	70,	76
	27,	36,	54,	108,	24,	. .,	. .,	114

Notice how the letters are arranged in the following square:

D L G S V

M H T W E

U N A X I

F R K C O

J Q B P Y

You will see that A comes just after N. C is just below X. H is between M and T.

35. What letter comes just before the letter that comes just below X?

36. What letter comes just below the letter that comes just before W?

37. What letter is midway between J and Y?

38. What letter comes between the letter between H and W and the letter between I and Y?

39. What letter comes between the letter which is just before P and the letter which is just above F?

40. What letter comes just before the letter which is just above the letter which is between N and X?

41. What letter comes just above the letter which comes just after the letter which comes between the letter just above H and the letter just below W?

42. What letter comes just below the letter which comes between the letter just after the letter just above M and the letter just before the letter just below E?

Look at this clock-face
The figures on the clock are missing, but you can see that the time is 10.15. The shorter hand is the hour hand.

Here is the same clock-face, but SEEN IN A MIRROR so that the hands look the other way round.

All the clocks below are supposed to be SEEN IN A MIRROR. You will note that each clock is numbered.

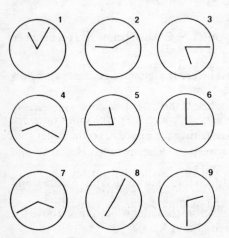

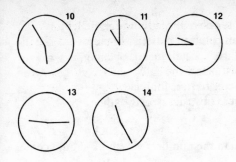

Look at clock number 7. As it is seen in a mirror the hands look the other way round, so that you will see it really says 8.20. So we write 'Clock number 7 says 8.20'.

Now fill in the right numbers in the examples below:

43. Clock number .... says 1.00
44. Clock number .... says 9.30
45. Clock number .... says 4.55
46. Clock number .... says 6.45
47. Clock number .... says 6.10
48. Clock number .... says 12.55
49. Clock number .... says 12.15
50. Clock number .... says 12.35
51. Clock number .... says 2.15
52. Clock number .... says 2.50
53. Clock number .... says 3.40
54. Clock number .... says 9.00
55. Clock number .... says 2.45

In the following lines find two words which mean the same, or nearly the same, and a third word meaning the opposite to the other two. Underline the three words.

56. devise, invent, destroy, listen, manoeuvre, study
57. static, emphatic, negative, electrify, positive, urgent
58. conceited, musical, unassuming, religious, colourful, egotistical

59. imprison, misplace, tuneful, agony, rapture, delight
60. tenuity, measure, halt, plump, plaster, slimness
61. ordinary, thoroughfare, special, metal, opening, commonplace
62. sweep, turbid, improve, barter, foul, clear
63. accelerate, rotate, free, obstruct, speed, lather

In the following examples fill in the numbers you think should come next.

64. 3, 7, 13, 21, 31, 43, ( ), ( )
65. 94, 79, 66, 53, 42, 31, 22, ( ), ( )
66. 1, 4, 3, 7, 5, 10, 7, 13, ( ), ( )

In the following, underline the word which would be in the middle if the row were in the correct order.

67. general, sergeant, corporal, colonel, private
68. gigantic, small, tiny, big, enormous
69. April, June, January, December, November, October, February
70. Z, B, A, Y, M
71. horrible, ugly, pretty, beautiful, ordinary

Looking at the numbers shown below you will see that all the numbers in the the lower row are connected in the same kind of way with the numbers above them. Fill in the two missing numbers in each row.

72.	4,	9,	3,	13,	11,	5,	10,	1
	13,	28,	10,	40,	..,	..,	31,	4
73.	3,	7,	8,	5,	9,	12,	6,	1
	10,	50,	65,	26,	82,	..,	..,	2
74.	8,	6,	5,	12,	17,	11,	29,	9
	21,	15,	12,	33,	48,	..,	..,	24
75.	2,	4,	6,	8,	10,	12,	14,	16
	10,	24,	42,	64,	90,	..,	..,	192

At 12 o'clock a woman starts to walk at three miles per hour. An hour later a man starts out from the same place and walks in the same direction at four miles per hour.

Answer the following questions.

76. At what distance will the man catch up with the woman?
77. When the woman has walked 21 miles, how far has the man travelled?
78. How far apart will the two people be at 3 o'clock?
79. Who will reach a distance of 13 miles first?
80. At what time will the man be one mile in front?

Six football teams enter a competition. The teams are A, B, C, D, E and F. Each team plays each of the others twice.

Can you answer the following questions.

81. How many matches will A team play?
82. How many matches are played altogether?

Now, if ten teams A, B, C, D, E, F, G, H, I and J enter a football competition and play each other once can you answer the following?

83. How many matches will A team play?
84. How many matches will be played altogether?

Now, if 20 teams enter a similar competition, answer the following question.

85. How many matches are played in total?

THAT IS THE END OF TEST B. IF YOU HAVE SOME TIME LEFT CONTINUE TO CHECK YOUR ANSWERS UNTIL YOUR TIME IS UP. The answers and the method of scoring are given on pages 71–2. The next test is Test C, the non-language (culture fair) intelligence test. It starts in the next chapter.

6

Test C

Explanation

To do this test you need not be fluent in English as long as you are quite sure you understand the instructions. You should get them translated if you have any doubts. Some very intelligent people will be able to get the idea from the examples. Test C is divided into four parts. The timing must be strict. Each part has a different time. For part one you have exactly three minutes.

Remember, you need a watch (preferably a stop-watch), a scrap pad, a pencil or two, sharpened at both ends, and a quiet desk in a warm comfortable room at a time when you can be sure of half an hour without interruption.

The non-language (culture fair) intelligence test

PART ONE

EXAMPLES

Instructions

See these examples for part one. In the first row there are four circles. The last one has a question mark '?'. In the next row there are six more circles. One of the designs in the circles is the most suitable one to go in the circle with the '?' in it, because it fits the series. In each of the drawings an arrow is leaning over a little more. The correct answer is circle 3, in which the arrow has leant over the right amount to continue the series. So the little answer circle has been filled in with a '3'.

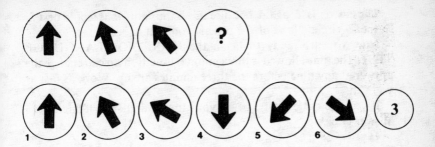

Now look at the second example.
The black section moves downward in the circles as we go to the right.
Now decide which of the circles in the second row is the right one and put the number of that circle in the little answer circle.

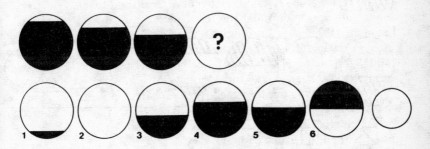

The answer is '5'. Did you get it? Have you got a '5' written in the small box that comes last on the second line?

In the third example the lines are being added as you look to the right and a hexagon is being drawn, one side at a time. Which of the six circles in the second row is the right one to continue making the hexagon? Write the number in the answer circle.

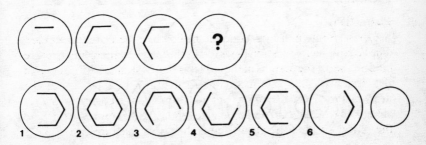

The answer is '5' again, because this is the figure that would best fit in the "?" circle. None of the others would fit as well.

Now you are ready to begin the FIRST NON-LANGUAGE TEST. The time allowed is three minutes exactly. You can change the answer at any time before the three minutes are up. Work as fast as you can.

If you are quite ready, begin your timing and start filling in the answer circles.

START HERE

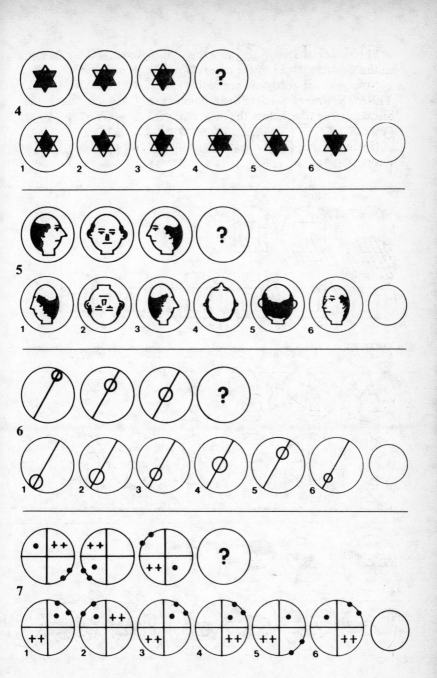

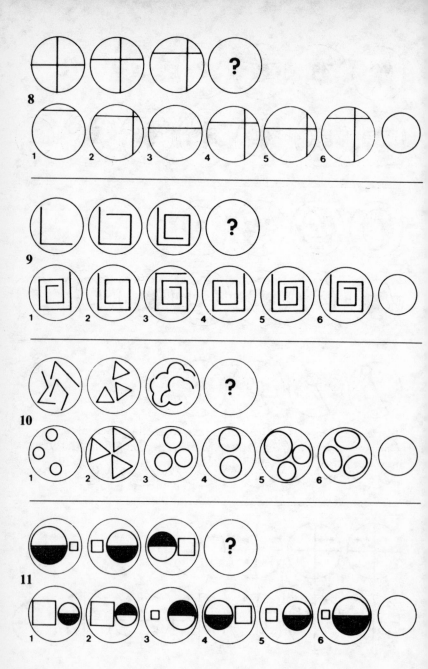

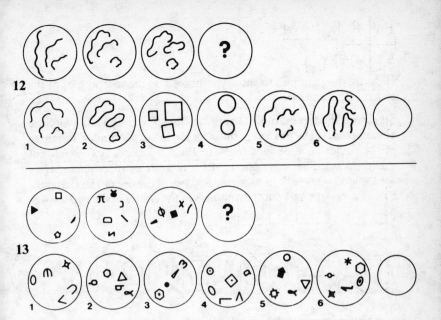

END OF PART ONE

If you finish before the three minutes are up, spend the rest of the time checking your answers. Then turn over the page in order to start the next part of the test.

PART TWO

EXAMPLES

Here are the examples to show you how to do the second part of the test.

Start with the top example. There are five large circles and two little answer circles. The designs in the large circles are all similar, but three of the circles have designs that are alike in some way (though not exactly alike). The designs in the other two circles are different. They are the 'odd ones out'. In each row find **two** of the five circles that have different designs and put the numbers in the circles in the two answer boxes.

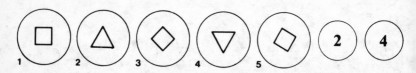

In the first example the answers are '2' and '4' because these circles have triangles in them and the other circles contain squares.

Now try the second example. The answers are '3' and '5' because these ellipses are shaded and the others are not.

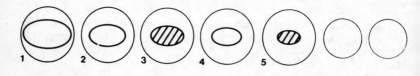

START HERE

If you are quite ready, start your timing. **You have exactly four minutes**. Now start filling in the answer circles.

1

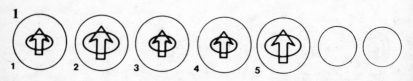

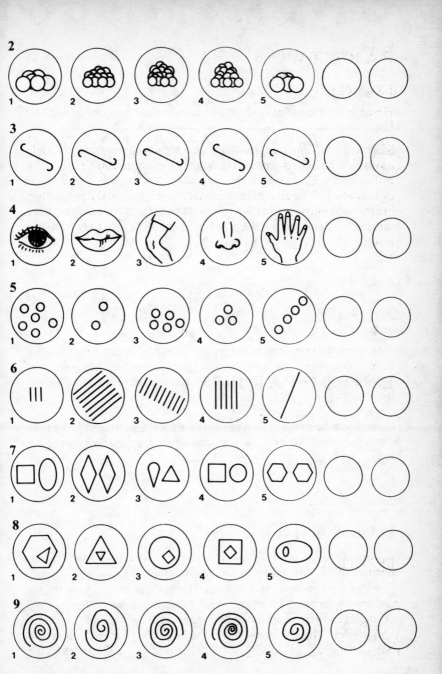

END OF PART TWO

If you finish before your four minutes are up, spend the rest of the time checking your answers. Now you are ready to start the next part of the test.

PART THREE

EXAMPLES

For this test **you have three minutes**. If you finish before your time is up, spend the rest of the time checking your answers. Here are the examples to show you how to do the third part of the test. There are four circles. Three of them have designs in them and the fourth a question mark, '?'. One of the designs in the group of six circles on the right is the one that fits best in the circle with the '?'. Which is it? You choose the best one and mark the number over it in the answer circle. In the first example the answer is filled in. It is '2' because that is the most suitable one to complete the group.

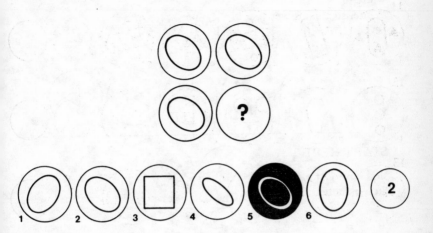

Try the second example.

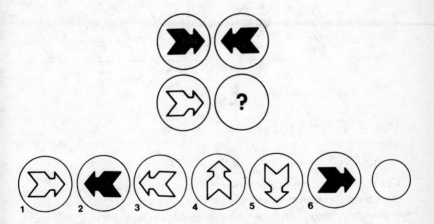

The answer is '3' because that fits in best.

In the next example, should we look for one triangle or two? One fits best. Is it white or black? White, so the answer is 6.

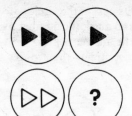

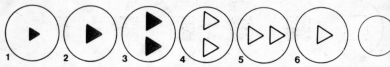

START HERE

You have just three minutes.

1

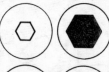

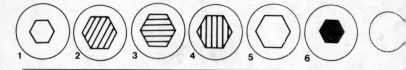

2

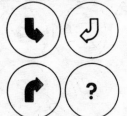

58

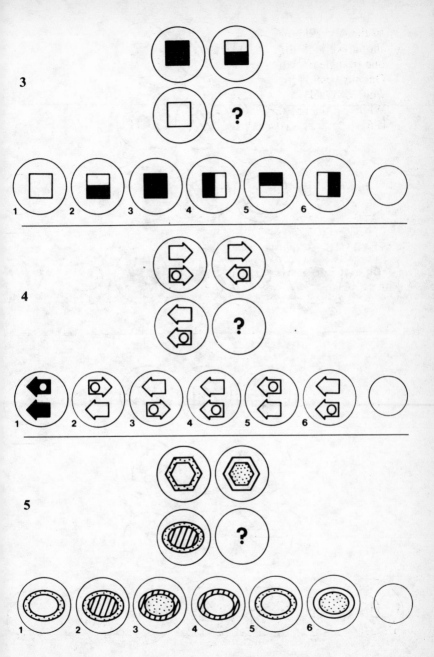

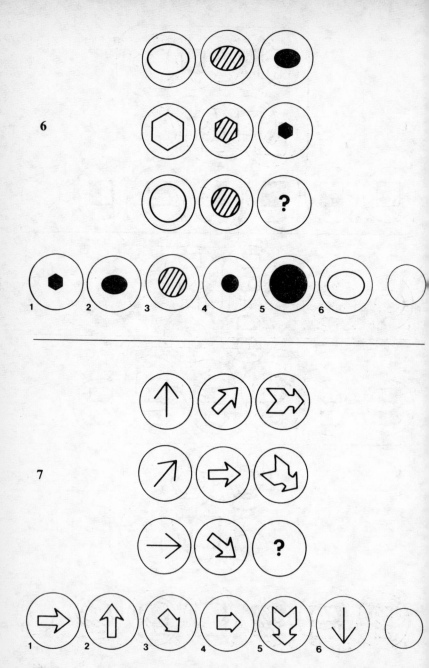

6

7

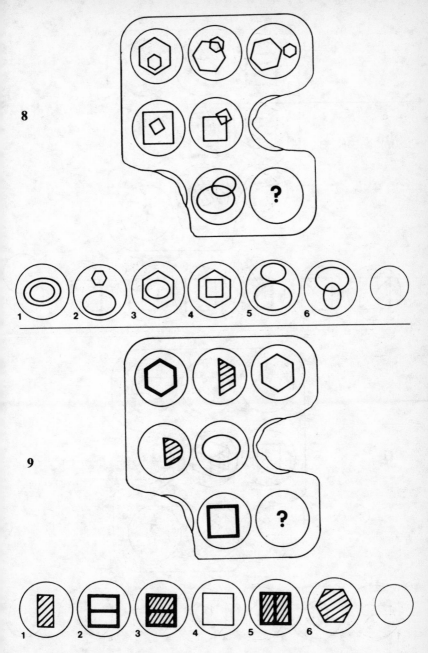

8

9

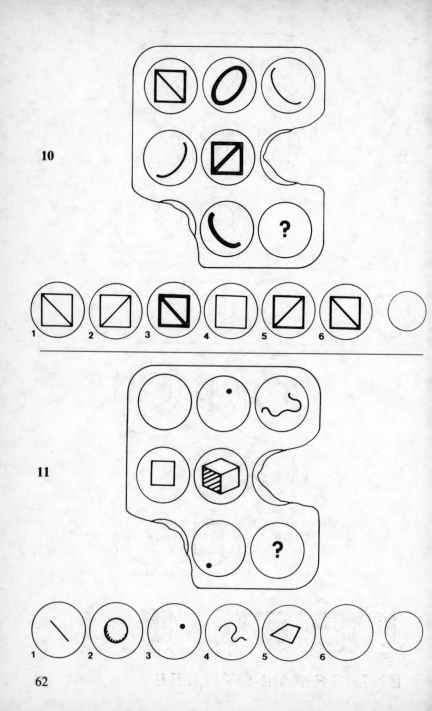

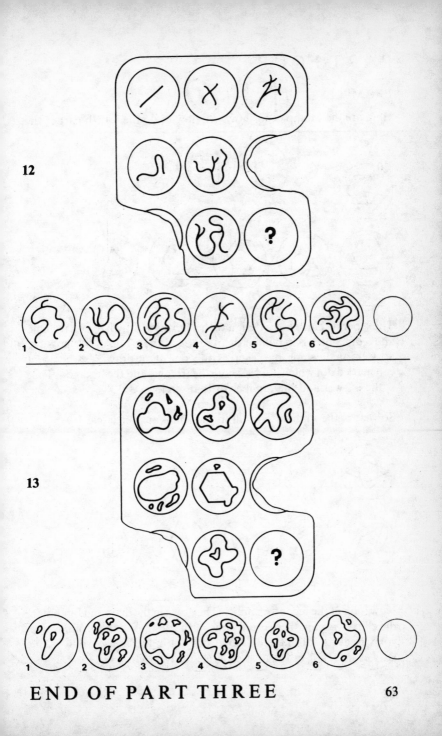

12

13

END OF PART THREE

PART FOUR

EXAMPLES

Here are the examples to show you how to do the fourth part of the test.

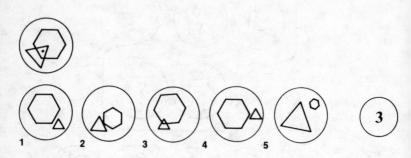

The separate circle has a design with a hexagon drawn over a triangle and a dot which is in *both* of them. Look at the group of five possible answers on the same line. There is only one of the drawings where you can mark a dot which is inside *both* the triangle and the hexagon. That is the answer and the number of that circle is '3'.

So that is the number you fill in the small answer circle.

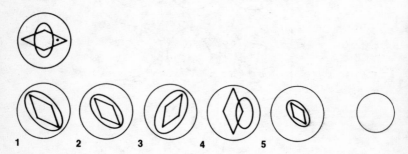

Now look at the second example. The dot is in the diamond but not in the ellipse. Again, there is only one of the designs in the group where you can get a dot in the diamond but not in the ellipse, so '4' is the answer. Mark it in the answer circle on the right.

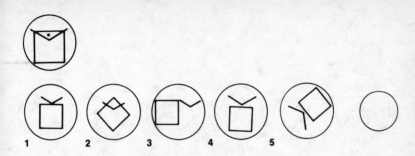

In the third example the dot is in the square above the 'V'. There is only one design in the group where you can put a dot in both figures. It is in circle number 2, so mark that as well.

The time allowance for this test is shorter. You have only **two and a half minutes**. Start timing, and fill in the answer squares as quickly as you can.

START HERE

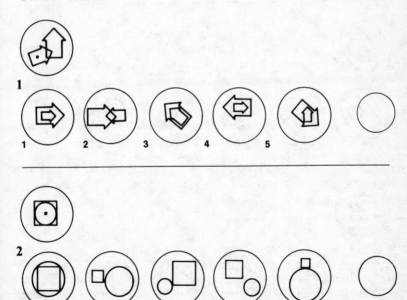

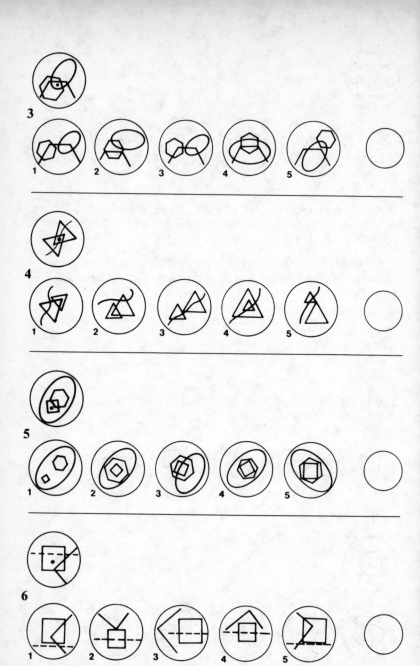

3

4

5

6

END OF PART FOUR

If you finish before the two and a half minutes are up spend the rest of the time checking your answers. THAT IS THE END OF THE TEST. Turn to pages 73–4 for the answers and the method of scoring.

7

Marking the Tests

The Answers

Here are the answer keys and IQ tables for the tests.

Answers to Test A (pages 34 to 39)

Word and number intelligence test (English)

1.	house	22.	13	43.	S
2.	potato	23.	10	44.	E
3.	hill	24.	5	45.	P
4.	metre	25.	15	46.	D
5.	crawl	26.	14	47.	potatoes buns
6.	scarf	27.	12	48.	walk listen
7.	16	28.	10	49.	gratitude idiocy
8.	21	29.	fruit apple	50.	short fierce
9.	15	30.	saw wood	51.	tomorrow
10.	10	31.	woman wife		instantly
11.	9	32.	ears hear	52.	36
12.	18	33.	kind cruel	53.	18
13.	3	34.	awake asleep	54.	53
14.	8	35.	black white	55.	25
15.	9	36.	liquid milk	56.	7
16.	6	37.	U	57.	49
17.	7	38.	A	58.	2
18.	1	39.	D	59.	1
19.	4	40.	I	60.	5
20.	2	41.	S	61.	4
21.	11	42.	D	62.	6

63.	3	73.	6	80.	Earth Sun
64.	8	74.	compliment	81.	century
65.	7		pleasure		second
66.	10	75.	sea island	82.	5
67.	9	76.	ear song	83.	10
68.	11	77.	then now	84.	2
69.	12	78.	peace war	85.	2
70.	13	79.	permissible	86.	20
71.	15		imperative	87.	40
72.	14				

Now add up the number of questions with completely correct answers. To be counted correct an answer must be exactly as given in the key above – no more and no less – except that in items 37–46 answers may be in block capitals as in the key, or in small letters. Answers to examples do not count.

This is your 'raw score' (number of answers completely correct).

This test is for adults and for this purpose you are adult at $15\frac{1}{2}$ years of age. There is a note on page 76 regarding children.

Find your raw score in the column below and read off an approximate estimate of your IQ and percentile figure.

Test A Raw score IQ table

Raw score	IQ	Percentile	Raw score	IQ	Percentile	
40	89	23rd	62	114	82nd	
42	91	27th	64	116	85th	
44	94	34th	66	118	88th	
46	97	42nd	68	120	91st	
48	100	50th	70	124	94th	
50	102	55th	72	126	96th	WORTH
52	104	60th	74	128	97th	A TRY
54	106	65th	76	131	98th	FOR
56	108	70th	78	133	98th	MENSA
58	110	74th	80	138	99th	
60	112	79th				

See Chapter 8 for an explanation of what the results mean, after you have marked all the tests.

ANSWERS TO TEST B (pages 40 to 47)

Word, number and graphics intelligence test (English)

1. vegetable
2. colour
3. animal
4. material
5. furniture
6. game
7. condiment
8. stationery
9. tree
10. instrument
11. footwear
12. County
13. mammal
14. small, little, large
15. sad, unhappy, pleased
16. high, tall, low
17. ugly, plain, pretty
18. flat, level, uneven
19. dull, dingy, shiny
20. foreign, strange, native
21. petty, trivial, important
22. 26, 30
23. 34, 42
24. 39, 36
25. 37, 43
26. 17, 16
27. O

28. Sun
29. hotel
30. Indian
31. 13, 9
32. 18, 21
33. 20, 24
34. 75, 105
35. K
36. A
37. B
38. X
39. R
40. H
41. S
42. A
43. 11
44. 9
45. 8
46. 3
47. 10
48. 1
49. 5
50. 14
51. 12
52. 2
53. 4
54. 6
55. 13
56. devise, invent, destroy
57. emphatic, positive, negative

58. conceited, egotistical, unassuming
59. rapture, delight, agony
60. tenuity, slimness, plump
61. ordinary, commonplace, special
62. turbid, foul, clear
63. accelerate, speed, obstruct
64. 57, 73
65. 13, 6
66. 9, 16
67. sergeant
68. big
69. June
70. M
71. ordinary
72. 34, 16
73. 145, 37
74. 30, 84
75. 120, 154
76. 12 miles
77. 24 miles
78. 1 mile
79. man
80. 5 o'clock
81. 10
82. 30
83. 9
84. 45
85. 190

Check your answers from the key above. Tick the answers which are completely correct and add up the number of ticks. This is your raw score.

This test is for adults and for this purpose you are adult at $15\frac{1}{2}$ years of age. There is a note on page 76 regarding children.

Find the line nearest your raw score in the column below and read off an approximate estimate of your IQ and percentile rating.

Test B Raw score IQ table

Raw score	IQ	Percentile	
36	**89**	23rd	
38	**93**	32nd	
40	**95**	37th	
42	**97**	42nd	
44	**100**	50th = average	
46	**102**	55th	
48	**103**	57th	
50	**105**	59th	
52	**106**	65th	
54	**108**	70th	
56	**110**	74th	
58	**112**	79th	
60	**113**	81st	
62	**115**	84th	
64	**116**	85th	
66	**119**	89th	
68	**121**	91st	
70	**123**	93rd	
72	**125**	94th	worth a try for Mensa
74	**126**	95th	
76	**128**	96th	
78	**130**	97th	
80	**132**	98th	THE MENSA LEVEL

Read Chapter 8 for the explanation when you have completed all the tests. See the same chapter for an explanation of what the results mean, after you have marked all the tests.

ANSWERS TO TEST C (pages 48 to 68)

First Part

1.	2	**6.**	2	**11.**	2
2.	3	**7.**	4	**12.**	2
3.	2	**8.**	2	**13.**	3
4.	4	**9.**	6		
5.	5	**10.**	3		

Second Part

1.	2 & 5	**6.**	1 & 4	**11.**	3 & 4
2.	1 & 5	**7.**	2 & 5	**12.**	2 & 3
3.	1 & 4	**8.**	1 & 3	**13.**	1 & 2
4.	3 & 5	**9.**	1 & 4		
5.	2 & 5	**10.**	1 & 5		

Third Part

1.	5	**6.**	4	**11.**	6
2.	5	**7.**	5	**12.**	3
3.	5	**8.**	5	**13.**	3
4.	3	**9.**	1		
5.	3	**10.**	1		

Fourth Part

1.	2	**5.**	1	**9.**	1
2.	1	**6.**	2	**10.**	4
3.	4	**7.**	3		
4.	4	**8.**	4		

Tick the answers which are quite correct and add up the number of ticks. This is your raw score.

This test is for adults and for this purpose you are adult at $15\frac{1}{2}$ years of age.

Find your raw score in the column below and read off your approximate estimate of your IQ and percentile figure.

See Chapter 8 for an explanation of what the results mean after you have marked all the tests.

Test C IQ Raw score table

The raw score is the number of questions you answered quite correctly in all four parts of Test C added together.

Raw score	IQ	Percentile	
19	91	28th	
20	94	35th	
21	96	40th	
22	100	50th	
23	103	58th	
24	108	69th	
25	109	72nd	
26	113	79th	
27	116	84th	
28	117	86th	
29	121	90th	
30	124	93rd	
31	128	96th	Worth a try for Mensa
32	131	97th	
33	133	98th	MENSA LEVEL
34	137	99th	
35	140	99th	
36	142	below here better than 99th percentile	
37	145		
38	149		
39	152		
40	155		
41	157		
42	161		
43	165		
44	167		
45	169		
46	173		
47	176		
48	179		
49	183		

8

What the Results Mean

First I must repeat what I have said before, neither doing better than you expected nor doing worse than you expected should give you any cause for concern. In either case you have had an indication which is better than your guess. If you scored very badly there is more chance of error. If you scored well and did not cheat a little you can be reasonably confident. In either event you can get a better estimate by applying to Mensa.

An IQ score of 100 is exactly on the average; 120 means you are fairly bright; 90 is a low score. University students need to be above about 125 to 130.

The percentile tables give a much better idea. If you are on the 50th percentile you are about average. Half the population would score worse and half better than you on such a test. If you are on the 70th percentile then 7 out of 10 people are probably less bright than you are; only 30% could equal or better your score. If you get above the 95th percentile it is worth a try for Mensa. The slight uncertainties of the unsupervised test may have worked against you. There is a test-retest variation of several points. The Mensa level is 131 – the 98th percentile.

The very best indication, of course, is to do all three tests and then work out your average IQ from the three results. It will be a better estimate. Here is how to do that.

Getting the best estimate, the average

Take the IQ scores from any two tests or from all three. Add them together. Divide by two for two tests or by three for three tests in order to obtain a better estimate of your general intelligence.

You can get your percentile rating from the table on page 72 by noting the nearest percentile that corresponds to your new figure, the average of your two or three IQ scores.

There it is – a first approximation of where you stand on the great IQ league table. Do not, I beg you, be too disappointed if you are no Einstein. A lot of us are not and we get on well enough. It is better to know your limitations than to delude yourself. But if you are brighter than you thought, as I once discovered, pluck up your courage and have a go. Intellectuals of the world compete. You have nothing to lose but your brains.

We all gain from healthy, enjoyable, peaceful and legal competition. I repeat, if your result really surprises you either way, have it checked professionally.

Children

These tests are not scored for children, but for older children or for very bright ones, you can get a rough idea in the following way. Find the child's IQ on the test. Say it is 85. Take the child's age in months. For example, a child of ten years and three months is 123 months old. The key number is 186. Divide 186 by 123 months.

186–123 = 1.512 approx. This is the key decimal.

Now multiply the child's score by the key decimal:

$85 \times 1.51 = 129$ (to the nearest whole number).

That is a rough estimate of the child's IQ. My other books, *Guide To Intelligence and Personality Testing* and *Check Your Child's IQ*, both give children's tests.

You can also arrange tests for children over six as well as adults through MENSA FREEPOST WOLVERHAMPTON.

9

So what is Intelligence?

Can you define it?

One of the arguments often put by the anti-intelligence lobby is that it is impossible to define intelligence and therefore impossible to measure it. Well, you could have said that about temperature before anyone knew that things were made of molecules that could vibrate. But it did not stop people knowing that there was some difference between the feel of ice and fire and even measuring it with a thermometer. Every language has dozens of words which show that the differences between people in thinking power were noticed long before anyone attempted to measure it systematically. 'Clever, bright, intelligent, quick, sharp, sage, brilliant, astute, shrewd, learned, sagacious, sapient, wise' – these fell out of the thesaurus on my word processor. There are a lot more. They are not all there in our language (and in many others) in order to refer to something unreal. We all assess the people we know and guess that this one is bright and that one a bit dim. So why cannot our judgments be compared with a tested standard?

Is there such a thing as intelligence?

Doctor Rose of the Open University claims that intelligence is what he calls a 'reification', a false reality created as part of the good old Class War as a means of doing down the dear old Working Class. There is no such thing, he says. I think we can confidently deny this curious notion. Many of the words above which express the idea of differences in thinking power existed long before capitalism started enriching most of us. Every one of us know the difference between a bright person and a fool. It is sheer perversity to say there are no such perceivable differences. (I think the 'working class' is a reification.)

A definition

I am not a great believer in the sacredness of definitions. There are lots of things we can think about and make sensible decisions about that cannot be defined scientifically. Define a table in a way that I cannot disprove by building something odd that meets your definition but is clearly not a table. Define an elephant or happiness. Difficult, but we can ride one while we feel the other.

In fact there *are* dictionary and psychological definitions of intelligence – rather a lot of them. And there is some disagreement between them. I have very a simple definition of intelligence as we usually use the word when we try to measure it. It arises from the study of information theory and practical, commercial work and thinking about the possibility of artificial perception and intelligence.

Intelligence is the power or ability in a thinker to acquire and use conceptual information so as to optimize behaviour.

I say 'conceptual' information because, when we talk of an intelligent human, we have a different meaning for the word than we do when we talk about an intelligent animal. A concept is an idea, an nameable abstraction. It can be represented by words or other symbols.

An animal such as a fox or badger or mole depends largely on perceptual information and past learning. What the animal sees, hears or smells is the input. Its behaviour is the output. It thinks like a tennis player or an acrobat. Messages from its eyes and other senses go straight through the brain to the muscles. There is no strategic level stage of cognitive or conceptual thinking. But we can think in words. We consult others in words or other symbols. That is the vital difference. It means we can do more experimental thinking.

The animal kind of intelligence can be described as motor intelligence or sensori-motor intelligence. We might call it skill rather than cleverness. It is very different from cognitive intelligence. Cognitive intelligence is also, and this is the real point, communicable. People can pass very complex thoughts from one to another in a way that no animal can. The noises, expressions, gestures and postures of animals tell each other about their emotions, not about their experiences or thoughts. They can express fear, rage, friendship, love, dominance, submission, and sexual desire. They cannot tell you where they have been or whom they met.

Cognitive intelligence

When you come to experiment with artificial intelligence you find out something that is a bit of a put-down for humanity. When we begin to look at how a bird manages to fly or an ape manages to swing from tree to tree without falling, we find we are dealing with a system of enormous complexity. The mere act of seeing and recognizing one's surroundings involves billions of nerves, each with thousands of connections. It is a system that makes the most complex computer look like a counting frame. The sheer volume of data handled is stupendous. In every living animal (mammal) it is far more than that handled by all the world's computers put together. Each eye has hundreds of millions of parallel inputs, each sending hundreds of signals per second.

Of course, you too have a very remarkable system. You use it when you walk or play football or do anything that you do semi-automatically without much conscious thought. But it is the other sort of thinking – the conscious, verbal, cognitive communicable thinking – that we most value, the thinking we can put into words and other symbols. Yet all that I think in that way I can express on this word processor in a few thousands of words, using a computer with a mere 20 megabytes capacity. In terms of information theory it is a much lower level of intricacy and complexity. How has this come about? Our vaunted, superior human intelligence is a much simpler information system and involves considerably less data handling than the system we need, or any other animal needs, just to walk around.

The secret lies in the strategic level. If we look at any great institution we are aware that some information is much more important than other information. The information being processed at the centre is a summated and concentrated form of the detailed, tactical level information being handled at the branches, the periphery. The same is true of the brain. The cognitive information, expressed in words and numbers, is a communicable, summated, selected, sorted, filtered, condensed and simplified version of all the other information upon which social action can be based. Essentially, cognitive thinking is social thinking. It helps to decide social behaviour, the behaviour of co-operating social groups. It is thinking on a higher scale. That is why we value it more.

Intelligence versus skill

Let me suggest another definition. Then I will tell you why it will not do. Scalar, or measured intelligence, is an indicator of the efficiency, speed and complexity of the reception and filtering of perceptual information and the degree, complexity and optimization of the resulting response behaviour.

This definition will not do because it takes no account of the strategic level, that is to say, the importance of the information dealt with. This would be a measure of animal, non-cognitive, psychomotor intelligence. On this scale birds and apes might beat humans and an athlete or gymnast would beat Einstein.

So for cognitive intelligence I finish with this. Scalar, or measured cognitive intelligence, is an indicator of the complexity of the cognitive input, the stored information processed and the speed, efficiency and optimization success evinced by the response behaviour of the subject or the social group influenced by the subject.

In this context 'cognitive' would imply strategic or hierarchical weighting of some kind. This would give success at making correct high-level decisions more weight than making correct low-level decisions.

Einstein would do better on this sort of measure.

Special abilities and general ability

It is important to make the distinction between special abilities and this factor of general ability which is expressed by the words in our language and by research in psychometrics. There are many special abilities such as the motor skills we have been discussing. But there are others, such as musical ability, which involve good sensory powers as well as motor skills – an ear for tone and a good sense of timing, for instance. You can also have a special ability at a purely cognitive task such as mathematics or playing chess.

Professor Spearman, who first worked out the distinction, put it like this. We all have our strengths and weaknesses at various cognitive tasks but there is an over-riding ability, which he called general ability, which affects all the other abilities. One child might be outstanding at maths, another at music and a third at poetry, and they might all be average otherwise. But the fourth is a good all-rounder, top in arithmetic and French, second in English, third in geography, second in science and so on. This child has general intellectual ability and that is what we are trying to measure on IQ tests. If you are good at music or some other special skill, and if you also have high general intelligence, it is an added advantage.

How we know that tests mean something

The reader might ask how we can really justify our confidence in intelligence tests. One way is to look at the professions people go into. We all have a pretty good idea which professions need brainy people and which can give work to those with average intelligence. There have been some researches in which the average IQ and the range of IQs have been checked against the jobs people do. The pattern is always just what you would expect. Doctors, lawyers, engineers, scientists, accountants and other professionals come out, on average, high. Labourers, packers, sweepers and lorry drivers, on the whole, come lower and those without work come out with yet lower scores. And I *do* mean on the average over large samples. I myself have done labouring and packing and even sweeping and I have been on the dole, but I was not all that dim. I am happy to say that, although most Mensans are in the range of professions you would expect them to be in, there are always a sprinkling of us in the less cognitively demanding jobs. What is certainly true is that most Mensans come from what would be called working-class homes. Professor Burt pointed out many years ago that the 'lower' classes have always supplied the majority of the intelligent. This is not because their members are especially bright but because there are a lot more of them, and intelligence is widely variable and scattered among all occupational and social classes.

Smart! why ain't ya rich?

The simple answer to this old taunt is that, by and large the smart *are* much richer. Several surveys in Mensa have shown this and they further indicate that Mensans show a strong tendency to rise above the social class in which their fathers were. Sadly, this is less true of Mensa women because, all too often in the past, a young, clever working-class woman married a lower-status man and took her status from her husband. There is a lesson here for women and for society in general. We waste far more bright women than we do men. (We also waste too many men.) We fail to find and use women's gifts. I am quite confident that this situation is improving but it still has a way to go. Undiagnosed bright but undertrained, under-used and under-promoted women are probably our greatest untapped mental resource.

Getting to be rich requires brains but it requires other qualities too. So by no means all the smart are rich. One thing you need to become a plutocrat is dedication. You have to make money your main aim and that is not always a very intelligent thing to do. And, unless you start with some great advantage, you also have to chance your arm and be lucky with it. The set of rich winners and the set of bankrupt losers are both subsets of the clever risk takers. In my experience, unless they have other serious faults, deficiencies or bad luck, bright people do fairly well for themselves according to their own desires, which are often highly unorthodox.

So what if you *are* a clever-clogs?

If you find out that you are a clever-clogs you might decide, as I did, to raise your sights, take more chances and be more ambitious. On the other hand, you might decide that you are doing pretty well where you are and that there is no need to take the risks that change always brings. Either way, do not let it go to your head. Intelligence is needed at all levels of our kind of society and it is no bad thing if some high-flyers are scattered throughout the community at all levels. But, on the other hand, when good opportunities do come along you might be encouraged to take a chance and have a go.

The one thing I can definitely recommend from my own experience is that you should never be put off by being told, or even by your own belief, that it is too late to try a new tack, learn a new skill or take on an unfamiliar role. Just as an example, since reaching 70 I have learnt to write programs for computers and have sold quite a few. I have learnt to work a word processor fast enough to write five full-length books and I have invented a successful board game. I had no experience of any of these skills before, and in fact I dictated all my previous books.

If you are bright, have a go: a carefully thought-out, calculated go. That is the essence.

Intelligence: Nature or nurture?

It does not suit the equality freaks to admit that there are such things as inborn differences, especially differences in anything as important as intelligence. So what has been obvious to hundreds of generations of people since the first civilizations has become a matter of dispute. People differ in a thousand ways and intelligence is just one of them. With all those differences we find that they are partly caused by the genes you inherited from your parents and partly by what happened to you after you were born. If your mother and father were both lanky your chance of being small is rather slim. But if you were half starved as a child you will be shorter than you would otherwise have been.

Everyone used to believe that human differences were affected both by parentage and environment. Not any more. We still all still believe this about height, weight, skin colour, hair colour and many other things but not about brains – that is too important. The equality freaks claim that there is no evidence that differences in intelligence within the human race are in any way inherited. Take any baby and treat it right and it will turn out to be an Einstein.

They subjected Sir Cyril Burt to a pretty thoroughgoing character assassination because he found out from work on one-egg twins that parentage plays an important part in differences in intelligence. They discovered errors and carelessness, exaggerated them into 'fraud' and spread the word that his work was entirely bogus. All studies broadly confirmed Burt's findings, but these inconveniences were ignored. And the word got around that intelligence is entirely unlike any other human difference – it is completely unaffected by the genes of the parents. My advice is not to give it another thought. Two things decide how bright you will turn out to be. The more important is the intelligence you inherited from your parents. The other is the way your family treated you as a child and the way your life developed.

When you were conceived the process took a hand of genetic cards from your mother and another from your father. The two hands were shuffled and out came your hand, a random collection from both parents. That is what you got in the genetic lottery. You could be unlucky and pick up a gene for Down's Syndrome from a forgotten great-great-grandparent, but the chances are you will be bright if your parents were bright and dull if they were dull. But the scatter is widespread. If you were lucky you could have two dim parents and be a high-flyer yourself. Or alternatively, a couple of high flyers could produce a slow-learning child. Both happen but both are rare.

The next question is what you made of what you got. If you were brought up in a home (never mind the social class) where there were books and stimulating talk, if you were encouraged and loved and stimulated by your parents and went to a school where they wanted to foster excellence rather than equality and if you turned out to be determined and studious and got enough to eat and drink, then you might turn out to be even brighter. If any of these things were lacking you might be a bit duller. That is the way of it. Intelligence is mostly nature, but bad nurture can spoil nearly anything.

10

The Importance of Intelligence

This chapter is going to be controversial. It reflects the views I advanced in my books *Brain* and *The Future of Intelligence*.

Being academically an outsider, one of those who lost out in the educational rat race and did not attend a university, I have had a very wide and therefore necessarily rather thin but very general 'do-it-yourself' education instead of the standard one. As a result I have wandered along some unusual thought paths. I crave your patience to see what I make of it all.

The greatest wonder in the world is mankind itself. I am overwhelmed with wonder at human intelligence at its best. Here we are, about five billion of us, crawling about on this seething planet. How do we come to be thinking and wondering about anything as remote and enormous as the universe? What is it, this Earth, our whole world? It is an insignificant, microscopic speck, buzzing round a minor, run-of-the-mill star, which itself is a tiny spot in a minor galaxy. The galaxy in which we find ourselves is 'the Milky Way'. To us it is an incredibly vast, whirling catharine wheel. But it is in fact just one more speck of dust in the universe, just one of countless billions such, each made up of billions of much more exciting stars than our humdrum sun. Yet here we are, we attoscopic men and women, each with a brain which we can use to comprehend and predict events in this incredibly vast whole. We can understand and foretell the course of this inconceivably remote system as it spins and whirls, explodes, implodes, and rushes through space squirting rays and gravity waves everywhere. It is as if a single blood cell in your body had the impertinence to think about the solar system and how it works.

The ladder of intelligence

Ernst Heinrich Haeckel was the first man to use the now popular word 'ecology'. He was one of the early biologists who digested the enormous implications of Darwin's theory of evolution. Haeckel noted the theme, implicit in Darwin's work, of evolution from 'lower' to 'higher' forms of life. He elaborated the idea of a *scala naturae* ('the ladder of life'), by which more elaborate, stable, co-operative and intelligent life forms evolved from simpler, earlier ones.

The hierarchy or pecking order of living things seemed to form a sort of progression, from simple bacteria, via eukaryotes (cells with a nucleus), to metazoa and metaphyta (many-celled animals and plants). Then there came sea animals like worms, then shelled worms and crustacea, crabs and insects, the hard-armoured creatures. Then came soft-skinned, backboned creatures, starting with fish, reptiles, mammals like ourselves, primates (the whole tribe of monkeys), then the apes and, finally, man. Guess where? At the top, of course – well, at the top of all we know.

Now we have to be very careful when we think in this way. It is of course very tempting for a species like mankind to arrogate to itself the primary role. Many modern biologists say that the *scala naturae* is an anthropocentric (man-centred) concept, which only man could have thought up. It is natural, they say, for humans to see humanity as the tops, so to speak. These biologists reject the concept and point out that a lot of species are better adapted to their environment than man is to his. This is good argument but it is not a proof. It leaves out of account the ladder of intelligence, of comprehension which moves upward, rung by rung, with the ladder of life.

Let us narrow our view and look at mankind on earth. Mankind has produced a number of fairly orderly and prosperous civilizations and, intermittently between them, a number of periods of chaos and hard times. During the civilized periods, though many bad things happened, there were advances in the arts, the sciences and in knowledge of the world and, generally speaking, intelligence and understanding came to the fore. In the bad days there was always a retreat of the spirit of mankind. Cruelty, oppression and tyranny ruled, and suppressed intelligence, the speciality of *homo sapiens*, mankind.

Our latest world civilization is the most widespread and successful so far. It was built up by brains and it survives by the power of brains. It would be a pity if we in this age were to despise and reject the one power in which mankind excels – thinking power. It would be rather like a conference of all the birds of the air which declared itself opposed to flying because of all the accidents that it causes. Intelligence is the human game, so let us play that game to the full. We should do as all the other species do, play our own hand.

I personally would go further than this. I look at the enormity of the universe and the insignificance of the little bit of it (that we know of) that has the power of understanding it – ourselves. One day we may hear of some other kind of intelligence that is a lot further advanced than we are. However, until we do there is absolutely nothing at all in the universe as important as the survival of mankind, with its magnificent powers of comprehension, because he may just possibly be unique in this respect.

While immodesty is a mistake, so is false modesty or mistaken modesty. It is not such a preposterous claim for mankind to be the most powerful, important, advanced and, of course, threatening life-form, on this microscopic Earth or even in this minuscule solar system. Let me explore this further.

The idea is that it is a rather splendid thing to belong to the one kind of creature that we know of in our tiny portion of the enormous universe that begins to understand and predict that universe in a really significant way. It would be rather sad if we all listened to biologists like Professor Steven. J. Gould and accepted our proper place as equals alongside the bacteria, plankton, worms and plants. I prefer to see mankind as the Earth species that has specialized in understanding as a way of life. I see humanity as engaged in a risky but wonderful experiment in living, which might very well bring considerable changes to this part of the galaxy some megayears hence.

Billions of years ago some pioneering creatures crawled up out of the sea and began the great occupation of the empty land by the life force. They would have been scorned as no-hopers if some modern biologists had been around. Some men or maybe much later on some much cleverer Earth creature will eventually take life and understanding up off this old planet and out in to many other orbits.

Climbing the ladder of life

Speculating on what intelligence actually *is* I found myself unable to accept the view that it starts with man. Conceptual, cognitive intelligence, thinking in symbol systems, certainly seems to be largely confined to our species. But it would be odd to deny intelligence to mammals and even to the reptiles. They manage to sort the world out, recognize the things they need to know about and adapt their behaviour so as to optimize their chances of survival as individuals and as a breed. Their psychomotor intelligence, adapting the motor instructions sent to muscles in the light of sensory information coming from the eyes, nose, ears, etc. is, as I have said, a much more complex task involving much more data-processing than thinking in words and symbols.

Once you start down that path there is no end to it. Once you see that all living things stay alive because they adapt themselves to their surroundings, you see intelligence everywhere. Intelligence is informed choice. When we fight for our autonomy, our freedom, we are fighting for our intelligence and our freedom to use our brain to improve our life.

The cleverness of cells

So where does cleverness start? Even cells have choices and adapt themselves, make small changes in themselves, move their parts about, move themselves and slightly change their form. Why do they do it? There seems to be a purpose. They do it so as to retain and preserve their basic living form and replicate so as to make more of the same. To do this the living thing, even the single cell, has to make the right choices. It has to smell out what chemical bits and pieces there are around it. It has to feed and excrete, take in this sort and reject the other. It has to get away from this place and move to that place where the chances of survival are better.

It does these things because it has knobs and bits on its surface which do for it what your eyes and nose do for you and other mammals – sort things out. One tiny protein knob spots something worth sucking in, another spots something to be avoided. Either way, the cell makes a choice and gobbles or avoids. It is discovering the truth about its tiny world and making informed decisions, just as you are. Intelligence is involved whenever any entity in the universe makes choices: not much intelligence, but a little bit. It is doing something no non-living system can do – well, no non-living system except one kind. Some human artifacts, things made by people, can do such things, but they were made by living beings in the first place.

Look at this more closely. What is it that is preserved when a cell continues to live? Is it a certain group of molecules? No. It is the form they take. The system is sucking in and spewing out molecules of all sorts the whole time. It continues like a fountain or a river: the form is the same but the content is always different. So the cell is not a single set of solid material molecules but a succession of different sets. I submit that it, the form, is not material; it is something else. It is the tendency of a form to survive with ever-different sets of material. And it continues because it appears to be able to choose. It has a sensing system which finds out what is going on, makes decisions and carries them out – just as we do.

This cell is far too small to be seen, but it is the first tiny rung on the long, long ladder of intelligence. Let us go up a few rungs. The bacteria were here on Earth first and they were all there was for an enormously long time, nearly 70% of the time since life began. Eventually they got together in communal (symbiotic) combinations and created the nuclear cell. These were the eukaryotes. They dreamed up a new system which speeded up the evolutionary process. Sex now reared its head. By getting together in a kind of gene-swapping orgy the little cells opened the door to the possibility of better, more viable forms. Sex throws up a richer variety of choices and evolution. The survival of the fittest does the rest. It picks out the fastest-breeding and best-surviving types. Evolution thus began to speed up. The next step was for these cells to get together in a sort of co-operative commune by clumping.

First they found they did better in various kinds of clumps than they did on their own. Then they began to specialize, these little cells, each taking on its own kind of job within the clump. The cell communities they were building up were the first simple animals or plants. They worked together and specialized just as employees do in an office or a factory. They set off another explosion of change and proliferation. Creatures developed which had billions of co-operating cells. These were the first plants and they obtained their energy from the sun. Others found ways to move about – they were animals. They got their energy secondhand from plants and other creatures. Being mobile, they needed better systems for finding out about the world – eyes, ears and suchlike. They had to seek out energy and nourishment, not just let it fall on to them from the sun or percolate into their roots. The chemical sensing and communications system used in cells and plants was not good enough or fast enough for animals. They gradually developed some specialized cells which dealt with communications –

the nervous system. And so they needed a sort of telephone exchange or communications centre. This was the animal brain, which now had a high-speed, electrochemical message-sending system, rather than the old slow way by means of chemical messages from one cell to the next.

Fishes

These moving life forms were a great success. There were worms of various sorts in the sea at first. Then some acquired a hard skin and all sorts of appendages, various tools and walking parts – legs. These were the shellfish and insects. By this time life had invaded the land. A very successful form in the sea was one with a soft skin and a hard but flexible central core. Instead of being armoured like the arthropods, they kept their hard parts inside as a framework. This made them less clumsy and much faster in the water. These were the fishes. They had bigger brains too. It paid them to be nippy and clever in the water.

The reptiles

Some of the more adventurous fish even adapted and crawled up out of the sea on to the land. They became the reptiles, the dinosaurs. At first they grew big and slow and were heavily armoured. On the land it was much more difficult to move about than it was in the sea where a waggly tail and a few fins would get you anywhere. Some reptiles found that it paid better to be small, fast, clever and supple.

Mammals

After a few million years the huge dinosaurs were overshadowed by a small branch, the nippy little ones which went in for a different lifestyle. They were small and fast, but the most important thing about them was that they developed a new and much cleverer central computer which overlaid the slow old reptile brain. They developed a better faculty for learning and adaptation, a good memory system for storing information, and an improved ability to recognize things and situations and react to them. On the whole they were clearly more clever. Another important thing about them was that they invested much more time and care in their young. The reptiles wasted enormous numbers of eggs, only one in thousands managing to reach the adult stage. The mammals' plan was to have fewer eggs and offspring and cosset their eggs inside themselves. The young were feeble and the adults had to invest a lot of time and trouble in them. But they had much more learning power; they were brighter. This meant that they needed more learning time and they could learn from the experiences of the parent animals. In the hard-shelled insect and shellfish the animal had to be born knowing everything it would ever know, because it was on its own from birth. Its knowledge and reactions were hard-wired and robotic, not flexible and adaptable. The reptile system was a little better and the mammals' system very much better. It left the individual animal more flexible in its behaviour, so that its reactions could be adapted very closely to its own circumstances, not generalized reactions such as would be transmittable by genetic heredity. Its parents could teach the young mammal not what was good for every one of the species but what was good in this particular valley and this particular climate, wherever they happened to be.

Primates

The groups of mammals that took these principles furthest were the primates – the little, sharp-eyed, skilful, grasping apes and monkeys – who lived in trees and could jump rings round most other tree-dwellers. Catching a monkey in a tree is a mug's game. Monkeys have a good memory, much like ours. They seem to be able to communicate a whole range of emotions and fears to one other, and they mostly live together in co-operative bands, as we do. They are certainly the most intelligent of the mammals (apart from humans), but they do not seem to have anything like the equivalent of symbolic speech or cognitive thought.

Mankind

Some climatic change, probably in Africa, drove a branch of these clever, vegetarian tree-acrobats out on to the plains where they took to hunting and eating meat and began to form hunting bands. Their well-developed climber's hands and excellent colour vision, together with the large brain they had evolved so as to help their teamwork were the magic combination which opened many doors of opportunity for them. They worked together in gangs to confuse their predators and their prey. Some of them started to do something no other mammal seemed to do – use something they could not eat to get at something they could eat. The climber's hands were handy for that. They used a stick to get at a fruit or a straw to dip for nectar. As hunters they had no tusks, sabre teeth or claws. But their folding front feet could grasp a stone, bone or stick and strike with it or throw it. With such a creature, so equipped, it was more advantageous to be clever and good at working together than it was to be large and fierce.

Thus there was an evolution towards bigger brains and improved communication. Tribes of young proto-men would chase and harry and out-think their prey, banging and prodding with sticks and bruising with stones. Men were fast, tireless runners because they had lost their fur and did not overheat. They could survive cold nights because they used the skins of their prey to cover themselves, cutting it away with sharp stones.

This life of hunting for meat and gathering any vegetation that would nourish them went on for some millions of years. They began to learn to use fire: some foodstuffs are eatable after cooking but not before. They used more and more tools – wooden, stone and bone weapons, skins, fabrics, ropes, pots and gadgets of all kinds – but only what they could carry as they wandered around.

In all mammals the best learning years are the early years, the years before maturity. Mankind began to have so much to learn each generation that evolution began to lengthen the learning time – childhood. A new-born gazelle has to be able to run with the herd within hours or it will be left behind for predators. Maturity has to be hurried forward; the learning months are few. But with mankind the children were protected, and could be carried and hidden by the clever tribesmen. Maturity could be delayed, so that there were five years, then ten years, then fifteen years of learning before the child faced the dangers and rigours of the hunter-gatherer life-style. Social life allows much learning and calls for bigger brains.

This went on evolving in a gradually improving pattern right up to the last Ice Age, only 10,000 years ago. By that time very advanced speech systems had developed and the stage was set for an entirely different life-style. Man had been becoming more territorial. Now he began to be a farmer and a herdsman rather than a hunter-gatherer. Instead of following the herds and killing at will he began to shepherd the sheep, goats and horses, to look after them and protect them from other predators, and to confine them and live on their blood and milk as well as their flesh. And he began to understand about growing food, how seeds work and how to dig and weed. The developing brain was opening new roads.

Civilizations

Settled life in one place led to the growth of villages. This meant even more social organization and social heredity. Rules, mores, customs and know-how were passed between generations with ever more accumulated skill, knowledge and efficiency. Village communities got into disputes about land and tribal wars broke out. Then they combined to beg protection from a free-for-all by accepting one leadership. They began to learn how to co-operate cleverly in order to fight one other. It was now that the evolution of intelligence in mankind was most favoured.

The growing kingdoms and empires could survive only if they could identify those who were capable of dealing with the complex problems that such an advanced social order called for. The societies that bred, identified and used the best brains had a better chance than those which did not. Civilizations and cultures came and went, but there was an accumulating gain. Once learnt, some things are never forgotten. The crafts – spinning, weaving, pottery, building, wood-work, stonework, metalwork – flourished and decayed, and moved from one region to another, but all the time they were improving and new crafts were being added. As civilizations rose and fell and rose again they always seemed to start from a slightly higher point. And all the time there was a quite unconscious selection in favour of cognitive intelligence. Intelligent people make successful craftsmen, scriveners and organizers. Tribes with leaders who could make war effectively and then conclude a sensible peace afterwards grew and spread. A tribe or a kingdom or an empire that valued its clever people, rewarded them and protected them would gradually acquire more of them – both through immigration and because of the children they would have. And, of course, the way they brought them up. Tribes that neglected their clever members were less viable, less successful. Some of the clever ones voted with their feet against such societies by migrating. If they remained, repressed and unprotected, they had fewer children. Thus, there was a tendency for the average intelligence to rise and for the tribes that fostered intelligence to spread further, be copied and survive longer. Meanwhile the database, the totality of what is known by mankind as a whole, was growing inexorably.

Industrialism

Then, unstoppably, came industrialism. Once the accumulation of knowledge and skills had reached a certain point, once communications between different human groups had reached a certain level of abundance and diversity, it had to happen. When they did come, the industrial and agricultural revolutions were larger affairs than what had occurred when the primates that were to evolve into men left the forest for the plains.

In a few centuries the whole world changed. Suddenly, the thousands of successful cultures around the world found out how to throw all the accumulated treasures of knowledge and know-how into an enormous common pool. The new world culture that was emerging from all the others in many places evolved an educational system. Thus, scientific and industrial practices arose which selected the most intelligent and empowered them to make the best use of the resources which had been accumulated.

Out of this came industrial mass production and an agricultural revolution which so increased production of food and goods that the number of men and women on earth rapidly increased. At the same time it made life longer, healthier and more pleasant for a very large number of people – more than the total world population a couple of hundred years previously. True, there are two other groups of human beings who have not yet managed to change their ways enough to share that prosperity. One of them is in the middle, probably better off than they had been before industrialism. Of the third group humanity is not proud. The prosperous ones feel guilty about them. They are no better off; they may be worse off. There are a lot more of them, and they are becoming more numerous. That is the problem which the brains of all humanity are called upon to solve.

This is a brief account of the ladder of life. It is an idea which sees some sense and direction in life on Earth, rather than a random and purposeless succession of accidents. It may not represent the truth, whatever that may be. But if life and humanity are the outcome of a long succession of accidents, then it does not much matter if mankind takes the mistaken view that there is direction and significance in the ladder of life and intelligence that Haeckel saw and I see.

If, on the other hand, there is sense and direction in the way the living, the biota, have been developing, if there is something good in the advance of the life force towards understanding and influencing the material world of the unliving, then we ought to be in favour of the advances in understanding that come to us. Mankind should be proud, not ashamed, of its well-developed brain. Men and women, while striving for a good life and a stable, peaceful civilization, should never lose sight of the need to preserve and further develop the wonderful world culture of knowledge, understanding and power over nature that the best human minds, with the help of all of us, have built up. The modern scientific and technological base of understanding and know-how is, in my opinion, a more magnificent monument to the spirit of mankind that any pyramid, skyscraper or Chinese wall. It is the biggest and best wonder of the world. We, in our age have things to be ashamed of, but we have much to be proud of, too, and that which should give us most pride is the enormous advances in understanding that we have made. Let us conduct ourselves in such a way that these advances shall not be lost in another dark age, but be preserved and improved so that mankind may go forward and, in the end, on and out into the unknown beyond our skies.

11
Fostering Intelligence

We are moving towards the end of an over-egalitarian age during which many intellectuals dreamed of themselves as the wise rulers and planners of an enormous, orderly, stable, prosperous, uncompetitive and centrally planned world state. I know because I was one of these happy, optimistic dreamers myself. Seeing the conflicts and inequalities of the world I longed for the day when reason, sweet reason, would rule our affairs intelligently. It would involve administration of course, but there were plenty of wise, altruistic men and women who could be appointed to work out what we all needed and to ensure that we got it. They would tell us where to work and what to do. The experts would work out five-, ten- and hundred-year plans using the best brains and all the discoveries of science. Then they would tell us all how to go about it. We would be told what, how much, and when and where to produce things – services, art, music – and where to deliver it. We would do away with vicious competitive commercialism and would use the best brains to organize us.

Everyone would take from a great common pool what they needed and desired and everyone would contribute to the great common pool to the best of their ability. 'From each according to his needs, from each according to his ability.' That was Karl Marx's way of putting it. (He seemed to think there might *be* differences of ability.) And of course it would be fair shares for all, the same for everybody, and no connection between what you put into the system and what you take out.

It was a very attractive idea and many sincere attempts were made in many places to make it work, but it proved to be impractical. There were two problems. Purely unselfish motivation works well in wars, revolutions and emergencies but it does not work well enough for long enough in periods of peace and stability. The self-sacrificing enthusiasts who took over the reins of power disappeared in many purges. They were replaced by bureaucrats and timeservers of limited intelligence. Alternatively, tyrants took over from the wide-eyed revolutionaries. There was no trial and error system which eliminated mistakes, proposed intelligent solutions and promoted intelligent people. Party hacks got the power and influence. The clever ones who thought up better ways and suggested changes got nowhere.

The centralist ruler – imperialist, fascist, communist or socialist – can get away with appointing loyal fools to control things. Even in a democracy, using the vote every four or five years does not ensure enough influence to eliminate incompetence. The pluralist firm or organization which fails to find and use its best brains will be quietly replaced by its competitors. It has to face the daily votes which we record whenever we spend our money. Our spending has an immediate effect and the market responds to our signals like an obedient dog. We are picking winners daily, breaking one boss and enriching another. In fact we are forcing the competitive business to use it brains. Unfortunately we are unable to do that with politicians.

Looking back at the succession of British governments, it seems that our cross-on-paper-votes have a patchy record at picking winners. Parliamentary democracy is the best central system we have, but the less mono-centric it is the better it is. Open, pluralistic, polycentric, free-market societies foster intelligence and put it to work effectively. Everyone is on his mettle seeking to improve methods before the other man does so. From this, in the end, we all benefit, because what they are competing for is to be the one who supplies and serves us with what we will pay for. Societies in which the rulers try to control everything from the centre are very good at wars. Such centralization works quite well for pre-industrial communities that depend on conquest and appointed local overlords. But by their nature they are prone to be overthrown by military coups and they are too slow and bureaucratic to run an industrial society. Their chief failure is simply that there is no competitive spur to progress at all levels. Without a war or a purge or a new revolution to stir their blood and their enthusiasm they begin to stagnate.

Intelligence, the peace force

It takes brains to win wars, especially modern wars, but it takes even more brains to avoid war without losing all that you value. It takes even greater intelligence to make a good stable peace after a vicious war. True, human intelligence has been responsible for the enormously increased destructiveness of war weapons, but it has also developed the defensive systems and methods we now use.

Where have brains been most successful? There is no doubt. You could slaughter a lot of people once with a good cheap sword or a bow and arrow you could buy for a day's pay. When you work out how much hardware it takes to kill a modern soldier inside his defences it comes to tens of thousands of pounds and many tons of metal and explosives per dead hero. I remember that even in World War I it took thousands of expensive high-explosive shells for each casualty. Technology is better at protecting soldiers than it is at killing them, but it does increase the destructiveness of wars. This is the bad news. Intelligence can be used both for good and evil. When communities settle differences between them by violence and war that is usually evil, and it is evil because it is stupid and unintelligent. Mankind has a large, effective brain, but he did live in competitive hunting tribes for a long time, and he was not clever enough to avoid having to fight other tribes for territory or starve.

So mankind, socially and probably genetically, is designed to be warlike, but war and brains are incompatible. War is such a stupid way of settling things that our species has had to find a way of switching our brains off before we go to fight. We have to work ourselves up into a brainless passion. We have to brainwash each sensible, prudent youth into becoming a mindless, programmed automat before we can turn him into a hero who will charge a machine gun with his rifle. We have to generate that communal madness which Lorenz called militant enthusiasm. I know. I was a soldier.

What science has shown us is that the biosphere is a unity and that fighting for a bigger share of it is the least intelligent way of obtaining one. It is fighting to get a share of a smaller, inferior cake. Fighting is controlling the population explosion in the least efficient and most expensive way. Negotiation and co-operation can enlarge the cake. Then voluntary population control or, preferably, at some later stage, space emigration can solve the other problems which cause war.

Industrialism shows that there is no real limit to the size of the prosperity cake, provided we do not destroy the towns and ruin the land that produce it by fighting over shares. Nearly all, if not all, the problems that cause wars can be avoided by human co-operation based on intelligence.

Do not worry about using up the earth's supplies. There is a whole, empty, lifeless, solar system out there. If we had spent the effort we have spent on war we would be out there now harvesting rare materials and establishing life and intelligence in other orbits.

Mankind is where the first amphibians were when they crawled up out of the sea and occupied what seemed to be the hostile land. Later most land was filled with seething life. I am in favour of life and the living. Are you?

Intellectual treason

The French use a phrase, *Trahison des clercs*, to describe intellectual treason, the betrayal of the supreme human quality, intelligence. The treasonable clerks of our day have opted out of *homo sapiens*. It is as though the swiftest, most acrobatic dolphins joined the League Against Swimming or flocks of swallows swooped around streaming banners from their tails marked 'Flying is Wrong'.

A significant proportion of several generations of the most intelligent and educated people in some parts of the western world have followed this strange and perplexing fashion. They dress up as labourers or tramps in tattered, untidy and unsavoury clothes and sprout long, dirty unkempt beards and hair. They carefully preserve or affect uncultivated speech in uncultivated accents. They have taken great pride in humility and make a belligerent and demonstrative display of intellectual modesty. They are frequently aggressive, bellicose pacifists and often call for irreversible changes in society in favour of this or that class or minority. They have striven with great success to forfeit all respect from people in general.

They bring to mind Belloc's ringing phrases, in describing the first of this miserable breed and contrasting them thus with their Victorian predecessors:

> Dons different from those Regal Dons,
> With hearts of fire and lungs of bronze,
> Who'd shout and bang about and bawl,
> The Absolute across the hall,
> Or sail in amply bellowing gown,
> Enormous through the Sacred Town
> Carrying from College to their homes,
> Deep cargoes of Gigantic Tomes.

I am all in favour of the massive self-confidence and outrageous pride of the Victorian intellectuals. They earned universal respect in a society that unashamedly favoured excellence. They were guilty of massive, justified intellectual arrogance, but they were in fact a splendid bunch, who set the world off on the biggest intellectual adventure there has ever been.

Brains versus bigotry

One thing I have noticed in my 40 odd years in Mensa is that we are relatively short of bigots. Certainly, we have them but they stand out like a sore thumb. Mensans are very diverse, protean and open-minded. They are quick to spot bigotry and put it in its place.

Bigots rather than villains are the unwitting devils of today's world. If we look around the troubled areas we will always find groups of zealous, contentious, single-minded bigots of opposite persuasions in the thick of the fray. What little brains they have are firmly switched off as they use their bombs and bullets in a hopeless attempt to change one other's inflexible opinions.

Idiotically, the opinions and loyalties always concern past divisions and disagreements that have become irrelevant in the modern industrial world. The Catholic and Protestant bigots of Northern Ireland, the Muslim and Hebrew bigots of Palestine, the Sunni and Shi-ite bigots of Iran and Iraq – what could they not achieve jointly if they competed to use their best brains to make the factories hum and the deserts bloom.

Bright bigots

It is the small proportion of bright bigots who are the most harmful because, having swallowed their main tenets for largely emotional or cultural reasons, they then put their good brains and command of words to work to rationalize their beliefs and dress them up so that they sound credible even to thinking people. The bigotries of ideologies and religions are like this. They have all had their periods of cruel extremism. Sad to say, they have always found men of outstanding ability ready to serve them in their worst and most inhuman excesses. However, and this is the good news, the long-term influence of intelligence is to damp down excesses of certainty and self-righteousness. Over a period of time sharp minds can pick the locks of the thought-prisons of bigotry. In the end it is always the clever ones who return to conditional ideas and the pluralistic competition of ideas. They find their way back to the real humility that lies in realizing the provisional and uncertain nature of all human knowledge and the essential tolerance and openness that is the preferred way for all really great minds. It is the bright who come to see that it is not given to us to know immanent and permanent truth. The surest truth is still 'the best we can tell at the moment'. The goddess of truth is a capricious woman. We may never be sure of her; we may never own her. We must be content with enigmatic favours when she smiles on us.

The educational levellers

The treasonable clerks I spoke of above are, many of them, also procrustean educational levelers. You will remember Procrustes, the classical Greek robber baron who insisted on equality between the travellers who passed through his valley. He wanted them all to be the same height in order to fit his bed. He 'abolished unfair and unjust inequalities in stature' by chopping bits off some people's legs and stretching others on racks.

With their 'progressive', 'child-centred', modern education, in mixed ability classes in enormous, disorderly comprehensive schools the followers of Procrustes have been aiming to turn out the British standard educated child. Scholastic, studious, intelligent children have been carefully put in their place and discouraged. The equality freaks have gained great influence in educational circles and, though their days seem to be numbered, there is a long way yet to go.

Enemies of excellence

Many members of the educational establishment seem to have become the enemies of achievement and excellence, with a philosophy that what all cannot achieve or will not be bothered to achieve shall be denied to those that can and have the will to do so. Every man and woman is unique at birth. They differ in many ways. The enemies of excellence seem to loathe the rich diversity of humanity and seek to impose everywhere a cloak of anonymous equality.

Tomorrow's world, compete or cash in

Only if we can maintain the peaceful and mutually beneficial competition of the market can we avoid that other sort of competition, the stupid wasteful sort, in short, war. There certainly are a lot of people who are not competitive, just as there are undoubtedly a lot of people who are very competitive. It is not a matter of counting heads and taking a majority view. These two kinds of people do not have an equal effect. Competitive people work harder, are keener, more motivated and will take more risks than uncompetitive people. They will always, whatever you do, be more effective, more influential. We have to accept that, for instance in any political system, the competitive and ambitious will rise to positions of power and influence. We shall be ruled by people who *do* compete whatever they *say* they do. That is the main reason why I prefer less centralized government, indeed, less government of any kind. I want the competition to work for me instead of against me. Commercial competition brings me cheaper and better goods and services. Centralist, national competition conscripts me and sends me to make war, and cause destruction and poverty. Make no mistake. Mankind will never be uncompetitive, but he might with luck become less warlike.

12

About Mensa

Let me enter a caveat. I am the Honorary President of Mensa International, but I do not speak for Mensa. No one can do that because we have no collective views. I write as a person and not as an official.

Mensa is a not-for-profit, informal organization with many branches. It is a very loose, world-wide association of people of all sorts who have only one thing in common. Mensans have all scored very well, at the level of the top 2% of the general population, in a supervised test of general (that is to say, cognitive) intelligence. The founder's intention was to build up a forum of intelligent opinion, a sort of an intellectual Gallup Poll and to do research on the opinions and attitudes of brighter people and compare it with unselected opinion. Nothing much came of that idea. But once a few people joined they began to meet regularly. When they did they enjoyed it so much that Mensa became a social club, a world-wide Good Talk Shop where people could argue and dispute, and discuss everything and anything without preconceptions.

No collective opinions

But Mensa is unlike any other organization. We are not united because we agree with any platform, point of view, programme or objective but because we were all bright enough to think for ourselves. Members come from all nations, all communities and all social, ethnic, cultural, religious and occupational classes. For this reason we have no tenet, cause, belief or view which we hold in common. It is not that Mensa has *no* views; it is that we hold *all* the views. We are a very representative forum and the better because we are often eloquent and literate; we can all express ourselves and our extremely diverse views pretty well.

Why it grows like a weed?

If anyone should know why Mensa, the high IQ society, grows like a weed, I should. But I do not. I can only make guesses. Only a small proportion of applicants are accepted, yet we grow like a weed. I am amazed by my success. There are times when I feel like the Sorcerer's Apprentice!

Mensa was founded in October 1946. It grew for some years and then began to break up in disagreement. When, in 1952, one founder had resigned as secretary and Dr Ware, the second of the founding pair, had left in disapproval, the society seemed to be in terminal decline. Imperceptibly I assumed the principal role in Mensa simply by doing the work. We had less than a hundred members left and they were scattered around England, and only about ten of them were active. Moreover, we had about £37 in the bank.

Working in my spare time, I recruited a committee and arranged a democratic constitution, introduced a bit of business sense and found ways to make it work financially.

I kept on being re-elected to the top job, so I began to spread the word abroad on my business trips and holidays. Mensa was never my main interest. I did what I could spare the time to do and I had no financial incentive. But, slowly and surely, other enthusiasts came and joined me in the work and Mensa spread around the world and flourished like the green bay tree.

Today we have about 100,000 members in over a hundred countries, numerous national and local organizations and a turnover which reaches some millions of pounds a year. We distribute magazines to every member monthly, publish books and provide help for gifted children. In the countries where we are strong, mostly in the western world, there are thousands of meetings a year for every social and intellectual purpose. The latest development is the sudden, great and positive interest in our activities in several countries in eastern Europe including the Soviet Union, Poland, Hungary and Yugoslavia.

We are weak in the Third World because of financial and organizational constraints and testing difficulties, but we are working to improve the situation.

What do Mensans do?

We have pub meetings, games meetings, special interest clubs, dinner parties, outings of every kind and international, national and local conferences on every possible topic – bringing together people from all social and occupational classes and from all races and cultures. Members have in common only the fact that they understand one another better than any other group of such diversity. This is because they are all bright and fewer of them than usual are bigots.

My guess at an explanation for this unstoppable growth is that bright people like to be stimulated, amused and challenged by others like themselves. Many of them are tired of hearing the doctrine of equality preached *ad nauseam* and would like to see more respect for excellence, even the least respectable, most hated and feared sort of excellence – intellectual excellence.

How to join?

If you want to join Mensa and manage to score anywhere near the 95th percentile on any of the tests in this book, it would be worthwhile to apply. You can get the home-supervised test from Mensa for less than ten pounds, or for what you can afford if you are not well off. However, if you are confident in your own marking you can bypass the home test and apply for a place at one of the Mensa-supervised sessions nearest your part of the country. Alternatively, perhaps you would just like to do a home test or a supervised test to check your own assessment or maybe you have a very bright child and would like to obtain an assessment.

In any event you should write to MENSA FREEPOST WOLVERHAMPTON asking for a test form. No stamp is needed. Put 'Child' on the envelope where appropriate. That is all.

13

About Gifted Children

Bringing up bright children

Many pay lip service, as I have said, to the ideological dogma that people are all born with exactly equal powers and potential. But anyone who has seen children grow up knows better. They are well aware that we human beings are very different from one another in many ways right from babyhood. And, happily, we diverge from one another, becoming more different as we grow older. What a boring, horrid world it would be if we were alike, all replicas stamped from one mould.

One of the differences between us lies in the speed at which we learn and the amount we can learn. Human beings vary in general intelligence as well as in special abilities. Now there is one thing I know for sure that may not be obvious to many people. It is something that half of a long lifetime serving Mensa and the Mensa Foundation for Gifted Children has taught me. The differences in general intelligence which we all observe can be seen from the start. Thousands of talks to members, to their children and to children who are members leave absolutely no doubt about this.

Babies who can read

There are babies who are very precocious. They can do everything much earlier than the average baby, especially anything to do with communication. They talk very early and soon command a large vocabulary. Many of them teach themselves to read before they are four years old. Some babies are able to read from flash cards at 18 months. There are children of two who can perform at the level of the average child of four. The brightest three-year-old children can talk, tell stories, draw and write at the level of the average six-year-old. They perform like children up to double their age. And it goes on like that right up to the age of 14. They start forward and they continue that way.

Think what it means. There are some, not many, six-year-old children who go to a primary school when they are already performing, or capable of performing, at the level of an average secondary school joiner. They are usually offered no alternative to primary school. They can read and understand a story book or newspaper. So they are taught the alphabet and three-letter words – a few a day. The system provides nothing for them. There is sometimes (not, alas! always) provision for the special needs of retarded children. It is almost unknown for advanced children at the primary level to get special tuition in the state schools. Many of them are compelled by the law to waste the next four to six precious, fast-learning years being bored to death and becoming either apathetic or mischievous because what is provided is of no use to them. The exception is always a nuisance to those in charge.

In proportion, there are not many of these very high-flying tots – a few percent. But the top 1% is the equivalent of about 20,000 a year starting at primary schools. Most face six wasted years. And we have to face it, they are the cream of the cream. They are the children who will become the workers who will be most important to us all in a society that functions as ours does.

Now, if cleverness can be spotted early and we want to find, motivate and educate as many as possible of those who are going to be the intelligent minority of the next generation, then we know what to do. Every community and society should be alert to find the promising baby as soon as possible – and do something about him or her. When we look at the problems that threaten mankind in the coming centuries we know we shall urgently need their services later on. Problems are not solved by goodwill and hard work alone. Human communities have to identify and use their best intelligences. This is especially so in an age when many of the traditional life-styles are fading away. Traditional life-styles contained much cumulative, trial-and-error wisdom – in fact much more than anyone understood. You do not need expert guidance to survive if you follow traditions that have been tried and tested over the generations. But once you start on that great experiment of the life force, that new idea, scientific industrialism and agriculture, as we did in the 17th century, you are going to be much more dependent on your wiser citizens, your entrepreneurs, your experts, your scientists and your sages.

The vital importance of early learning

In the past educationalists have tended to assume that learning was a process that speeds up as you go forward. The more you know, the faster you learn. On the surface it looks like that.

But, from an unexpected quarter there comes a strong suspicion that that idea may be quite wrong. Strangely enough, it is the unsuccessful attempts (so far) to create artificial intelligence by computer experts that have revealed that the reverse is probably true.

We have known since Binet that mental age has a limit at between 14 and 18 years. We also know that it actually declines slowly after maturity is reached. We are well aware that it is the younger ones who excel in the most difficult fields of mental endeavour – mathematics, fundamental physics, cosmology etc. The new ideas and directions in these disciplines come from the young. What we have not realized is that this may be a general truth about learning. It is fastest at birth and slows down every year thereafter. We are deceived because we have never realized how difficult the early learning of a child really is.

In just a few years it has to learn first to perceive and recognize what it perceives. Seeing, recognizing objects and sounds, is taken for granted. We have forgotten how we learned to do it. But in terms of information theory it is enormously difficult and so far inexplicable. Just learning to recognize any familiar object, any chair, cup, shoe or other item, in spite of the enormous variability of the thing itself and the way it appears on the retinas of the eyes – at different times, in different lights, from different angles – is a problem of enormous proportions. What any baby does is completely impossible for the most advanced computer.

There is a lot of tactical level primary learning of this sort to be accomplished before the child acquires words and so can obtain guidance from its parents. But an intelligent child can learn a language, in fact several languages, if it is exposed to them in three years or so. Once it has got to the strategic level, as it were, once it has a vocabulary of words and can begin to ask questions and learn from others, the process *seems* to speed up but it is only because the child has better communications, not because it is learning faster. The infant is now dealing with a limited number of concepts and percepts with symbolic representation by a few thousand words. When the baby started it had to contend with an enormous informational bombardment from all its half a billion sensory inputs. And the tiny tot had to learn to manage, separately, a million muscle fibres.

At the more central levels – the strategic levels of mental function – where thinking is in words, the child's data input is a few score words a minute. At the outer, tactical levels, where perception and recognition occur the brain is processing signals from nearly 500 million parallel inputs per second. This is the number of visual receptors in its two retinas and its many other receptors of sound, touch etc., when it is learning to see, hear and feel. Learning to filter and understand that bombardment of information and learning to send the right messages to its million or so muscle fibres in order to walk and talk, is a much more difficult task. Learning is incredibly fast at this time.

The point is this. Early education is the most important, especially for the bright child. That is probably the reason why, even when matched for IQ, children from homes where they get a lot of attention from parents, where there are books and intelligent conversation, where the child mixes with educated people, do much better later.

Many social thinkers ascribe these differences in scholastic progress to the 'social deprivation' of the 'working class' homes, by which they mean those homes in which the children get less stimulation and less exposure to education. Give the poor workers more money they say and all will be well. But the enormous increase in the affluence of all social groups today has made no difference to the facts. The truth is that education has a cultural component and a social as well as a genetic heredity. Some families pass on the desire for, and early experience in, education as well as the genetically better brains to deal with it. And those families are found in all social and occupational classes. They are found in all communities and among the minorities, too. It is untruthful, as well as an insult to all other groups, to suggest that they are to be found only in rich, white, middle-class homes. What may be true is that, in a fluid, pluralist society, those families with either high native intelligence, strong educational traditions, or both, tend to move into what are judged by most to be 'higher' social situations. What that means is that, in the public perception, they are doing tougher jobs, which call for more study, training, intelligence and hard work. Those who are in sub-cultures that suit the life-style of that community are bound to do better in it.

Do precocious children burn out?

Some educationalists actually try to damp down and limit childish precocity because they believe that it often 'burns out'.

'Do not let the child overstrain its brain', they say, and insist on the convenient practice of teaching all children of the same age at the same pace and in the same way. The facts are that the overwhelming majority of the children that show advanced talent early *do* fulfil that early promise. They go on to great achievements if given half a chance. A child should be allowed to set its own pace. There should be no holding back.

Self-fulfilling prophecies

We hear a lot about the experiment which allegedly proved that, if teachers are told that a slow child is bright, this improves the child's performance. Sadly, there is nothing in it. It would be marvellous if all we had to do to make a dull child brighter was to tell the teacher that it is so. There is however, a real self-fulfilling prophecy. If a teacher believes that precocity burns out and accordingly holds the child back, it is bound to slow the child down, in comparison with the child whose teacher rejects this nonsensical idea. A reduced challenge does produce a poorer education.

The real and visible danger is that very intelligent children in the standard mixed-ability school are being frustrated by being held back. They become bored and either passive or mischievous. In a class where they get no challenge and no competition, and where they attract envy from the other children because of their effortless superiority in learning, they frequently cover up and opt out of the whole process.

Inattention, daydreaming, mischief – these are the results of confining an active, enquiring, super-intelligent child in a class where the pace is decided by the teacher's correct concern for the slow learner. The child can be put off the whole education process for life.

Are swots feeble?

Another myth in this area is the notion that the clever child is usually a weak, weedy, spotty specimen. That is a stereotype which is at odds with the facts. It seems to have arisen from a sense that nature is trying to be 'fair' and is distributing advantage and disadvantage on the basis of equity. Societies and communities can do this; it is what they are for. But nature always chooses winners when it can.

The depressing fact is that there is no law of compensation by which those who are bright are handicapped with knock-knees and spots. Nor are those who are good at one thing handicapped by being bad at another. The general truth is as Professor Lewis Terman discovered: bright children have the full range of differences in all other aspects but there is no tendency to compensation. Indeed, there is a definite trend for the brighter and more successful children to be on average, taller, more healthy and more athletic. The head boy is much more often *victor ludorum* than the myth would allow. Nature should be severely condemned by thinking people for displaying such unfairness.

Mixed ability or mixed ages

As I have said earlier, one of the things that wastes a lot of talent in this country is the mixed ability class. This untested innovation was introduced in the silly 60s and is still widely practised in the state sector of education in Britain.

In traditional societies the mixed-age group is natural and normal. In the extended family group every generation from sucklings to great-grandparent mixes in happy and fruitful interaction. There are no complaints that the different stages of mental and emotional development of the people in a large family cause grave psychiatric problems. Certainly, the children prefer to play together and learn together some of the time, but there is no segregation by exact age.

State education is a new idea which is hardly more than a 100 years old. We can see that it was administratively convenient to take in an age class as a unit and put them through school together. That is what was done in Britain. However, when we are told by 'experts' that to mix children of different ages in one class will do irreparable emotional damage I find myself totally sceptical.

We were all kept in one age group in class at my slum district school in the 1920s, but we immediately mixed in all groups in the playground. I dare say it is much the same today. But I have heard people seriously claiming, in defence of the present system, that it is fatal to put a bright, forward child into a class to learn alongside older children of the same mental age.

On much of the continent and in many schools in the United States they seem to do just that. They put children in classes according to their mental age or their progress in school. Thus, the child can continue to develop freely without being held back by slower children in the same class. Education goes by stages not ages. It is not a matter of the odd bright child in a class of older ones. All the classes have a spread of ages – the normal human pattern. But each child is in a class where there is real competition and stimulus, where progress is continuous and where the subject matter and the level of discussion are within every child's reach.

The statistics are unambiguous. The educational results of this system are very much better and the emotional traumas predicted by some 'opponents' simply do not happen. At the John Hopkins University, which specializes in very able mathematicians, they will take children of ten into classes of adults if they are ready for that level of instruction. There are no unusual problems and the graduates emerge as a very successful bunch. Schools, universities and industries all over the world are competing to get the services of the graduates from John Hopkins University.

'Select' schools?

One of the frequent complaints made by some members of the teaching profession in this country is that private and public schools are 'creaming off' the bright pupils from other schools and thus, it is said, doing harm to the other students and to the whole educational system. This is one of those ideas that gain currency by repetitive assertion rather than by argument or evidence, so it is rather hard to refute it.

It requires a feat of the imagination to think how it benefits any slow-learning child for another, brighter child to be bored and frustrated, pretending to be working on a syllabus it has long ago mastered. That able child is at the school by compulsion; it has in effect been conscripted. If it is to be confined for six hours a day, the child and its parents are entitled to expect that it is deriving some benefit. It is not conscripted like a soldier to serve in a time of national peril. It is not there to serve the interests of the other children, but to prepare itself for its own life, so as to contribute in the best capacity it can. It is not for teachers to share out the talent between them on a playground morality system. They are there to serve the children and they will do that best if they learn to specialize, as all other professionals do. Some teachers can be very good at dealing with slow learners; some can get the hang of helping the average ones; and others can do their best for the brightest and most studious. These are the pupils who can make the best return on the investment in time, care and money.

It is right, in a very mixed society, for children of all sections of society, all ethnic, religious and social groups, to meet and mix, for parties, for entertainment, for sport, for religious and social purposes and for meetings. But for the very important business of academic instruction children should be in groups chosen for academic ability, progress and potential and nothing else. To mix slow learners and very bright children in one class at school is to harm both. At one end the children give up in despair because they see no hope that they will ever cope. At the other, without the stimulus of competition, the bright ones become lazy or disguise their ability in order to avoid the envy of their peer group or even their teachers. Learning is a serious business. It should not be corrupted by people who want to use schools for the purpose of social engineering.

Elitism and anti-elitism

'Elite, the choice part, the best' (*Concise Oxford Dictionary*). When I appear on a radio or television programme I am always waiting for the routine question about Mensa: 'But is it not rather an elitist organization Mr Serebriakoff?'

I usually reply: 'We are not an elite of power or privilege, of course, but it would be churlish to spurn your kind compliment. We are chosen by psychologists for intelligence.'

Elite means 'chosen'. There are natural and proper objections to self-chosen or self-perpetuating elites, but a true elite has been chosen because of its merits and its usefulness.

The idea that our complex, interacting society could function properly without groups which are selected and labelled because of their special ability to serve is quite absurd. If we followed the advice of the more extreme anti-elitist ideologues we should have no doctors, engineers, teachers, lawyers or experts of any kind. The last serious attempt at practical anti-elitism was made by the Khmer Rouge in Cambodia. Eliminating the elite in that country did no good. Millions died and the survivors remain impoverished.

We should not envy and decry elites but make sure that they are chosen on grounds of merit and ability to serve us well. We all need the service of elites and the aim should be to improve them, not eliminate them.

The way to do this is beautifully simple. We have to insist that it is we, the public, individually, who do the choosing. Elites imposed by the state are usually worse than those which arise from public choice. If elite groups offer themselves collectively, like doctors and lawyers by grouping themselves in a single association, we still have choice but we are forced to choose from among their accepted members. It is much better when there are a number of certification associations as with accountants. The groups compete to build up the best reputation, so that we choose both the association and the individual from it who is to serve us.

The more there is choice, the more free the choice, the better it is. Elites that are not chosen by the way we spend our money or the way we cast our votes are not elites at all; they are oligarchies. Most communist countries are run by self-perpetuating oligarchies, but reform is in the air.

Privileged intelligence or intelligent service?

To summarize, I see intelligence as a social phenomenon rather than an individual one. Intelligence in the sense we discuss here is the development of symbolic thinking and this came about so that human groups could exchange thoughts. Intelligence is there in the tribe or group to serve the tribe or group. It serves the group more than it serves the individual who happens to possess it.

Primitive tribes who had a few clever members, took notice of them and encouraged them, did better, lived better, prospered and left more descendants than others. The intelligence of the few thus serves the many. Only social animals such as ourselves are likely to benefit from a large and efficient brain and what goes with it – a very long and risky period of immaturity.

We ought to see our bright ones as an asset and do our best to exploit that asset for the general good. We have to face the fact that the bright have an extra burden and responsibility. Every person's rights should be equal, but their responsibilities must be in accord with their capacity.

Furthermore, there is a sense in which intelligence is expendable.

The intelligent entrepreneur and intellectual are often the ones in any community who use their brains to think up new, innovative options and ideas. In well-organized societies it is the general public which makes the choice between these options. And in the world of innovation and progress, many are called but few are chosen. The intelligent have the chance to choose. They may take the risky path of seeking beneficial innovation and accept the long odds against success, or they may opt for the less exciting but comfortable life of just doing some job very well. They are lucky to have that option.

My conclusion is that we should stamp on the idea that it is an unfair privilege when bright children are educated by specialist teachers. It is not immoral to bring together children who can stimulate, challenge and help one other to make the best of themselves, so that we shall have a cadre of intelligent, trained workers in the future. Education is an unpaid service, not a privilege. The young citizen is conscripted to prepare himself or herself to serve in the most difficult and demanding roles of which he or she is capable. The service they are spending their time and using their talent to prepare for is service to their community and their country as well as themselves. We shall need them more than they will need us. We should wish them well in their studies and let no ideological prejudices hinder them. We owe them a debt, merely because we ask them to spend more years in unpaid study rather than in paid work. They will be doing a more difficult job than many of us could contemplate.

14

The Future of Intelligence

From all classes and races

I have made this point before but it cannot be stressed too much.
Thinking of the future of intelligence on this tiny planet and out there
in the universe we can forget the idea of a superman or a super race. All
races of men have the full range of ability.

One scheme for the future of man was the socialist dream, and H.G.
Wells inspired many with his vision of a world governed by reason,
instead of by the traditional ruling classes.

I spent most of my early intellectual life as a sincere and active
socialist. I saw a world in which, instead of the unplanned scramble
and wasteful competition of modern commercial capitalism, there
would be a splendid, compassionate, egalitarian, centrally planned
world state, governed by the best in human thinking.

However, that vision faded and the intoxicating dream of building
socialism on the foundation of one discontented social class took
over. It happened just at the time when that class, the manual workers,
began to be replaced by automation.

One of the great failures of the socialist movement was the way its
intellectuals, (who came from all social classes) confused mental
excellence and intellectual values with differences in social class.
Many of them threw out the baby of intelligence with the bath-water
of what they called 'ruling class' bourgeois values. The bourgeois were
rated as clever, so cleverness was bad. Actually the bourgeois are, like
any other class, mixed.

When they assumed power socialist governments tried to make a
great, planned society. It was to be controlled from the centre by
human thinking power rather than by the traditional structures or by

the pluralist market which had grown up.

If ever there was a time for the fostering of intelligence it was then. But we were all too interested in closing down 'middle class' grammar schools and herding children – clever, average or retarded – into mixed ability classes in comprehensive schools. We wanted those incompatibles – complete equality, affluence and justice.

The early socialists had been on a different tack. They did their best to educate any clever working man to the highest possible level. They cheered when any brilliant child of humble background was 'creamed off' by winning a scholarship to a 'selective' secondary school or to a university.

But against all odds, we achieved the great goal – national ownership of some of the 'means of production, distribution and exchange'. And what happened? The nationalized industries came under the control of third-class minds, party hacks, aged civil servants and suchlike. The civil servants had not been trained as entrepreneurs; they had been trained to control and limit them.

The taxpayers of the diminishing private sector soon found themselves paying their taxes to subsidize great monopolistic state industries, as they slid into slack, inefficient, unenterprising, muddle and loss. We socialists had the will but we had not got, could not find, the excellence, the brains and organization to make our big ideas work.

In the early days socialism had an enormous appeal to the intelligent. As a factory worker, it was that that attracted me to the labour and trade union movement. I did not want to 'win the class war' and 'smash the class enemy', I wanted to put the best rational thinking in charge of human affairs. Those who were attracted by class envy were usually both dim and weakly motivated, but the clever ones were the altruistic enthusiasts who gave up everything for the cause. 'Let reason rule' was our socialist cry.

What was wrong was simply the idea that being an intellectual, being clever and interested in general questions was 'middle class' or 'bourgeois' and a betrayal of the working class. Middle- and upper-class opinion had ascribed mental inferiority to the working class movement and since many of the socialist intellectuals were middle class, the stereotype was accepted even in the movement. Deep down and unacknowledged, we had accepted the libel that the workers were none too bright.

There is a similar problem with regard to ethnic origin. It is very usual for human beings to ascribe stupidity among many other faults to the outlander, the stranger, to those from another culture who look different. It usually is the intelligent and educated of every culture who first discover and accept the truth, that each identifiable ethnic group has the full range of human differences. All races have idiots and geniuses and everything in between. I suppose it would be extraordinary if the average intelligence of different groups happened to be identical.

It is very difficult to ascertain this because there are no tests which have been standardized on the whole of humanity. And, moreover, it is of no more importance than the fact that the average height of Scandinavians is greater than that of Japanese. It is statistically certain that the within-race differences in intelligence are much more important than any differences in between-race averages. The worst kind of intelligence test is that involving a skin colour or eye slant inspection.

However, it is not surprising that a stereotype of white race superiority arose. It was not only the whites themselves that believed it. Around the middle of the 19th century certain European nations industrialized themselves, thus becoming economically and militarily powerful. In accordance with the morality of the time they colonized many other lands.

People that are successfully invaded by affluent, powerful strangers with terrible, new weapons, effective machines and better ways of making and doing things may hate them but they also grant them a grudging respect. And the invaders find it easy to agree with the natives' over-modest views.

The corrective has been brought about by means of cheap modern transport and by the natural counter-invasion – the emigration of people from the preindustrial to the industrial world. Once people from different countries really began to mix we discovered that the stereotypes were false.

That view has gradually permeated all the societies which are faced with this problem. I can affirm that in my 40 years in Mensa I have never seen any discrimination on racial grounds. The only exception occurred in 1948, when at one meeting a member proposed a rule preventing black persons from joining the society. After a stunned silence another member moved an amendment: 'That the word "black" in the motion should be replaced by the phrase "red and green striped"'. In that form the colour bar was passed.

The ladder of life

Let us look back again at the idea of the ladder of life, the idea that intelligence, sapience and understanding is the name of the strange game that is being unconsciously played in the universe.

The advances that have been made in biology, in the life sciences in the last 50 years have been just as staggering as the advances in fundamental physics in the first half of the century were and, in more senses than one, earth-shaking. We are beginning to see that life is other; it is very different indeed from the non-living, the purely material world.

The material world seems to be very predictable. At our level of observation it is subject to strict laws. The world of the living on the other hand is extremely unpredictable and complex. The ecosystems have an entirely different kind of mutual relationship from that which prevails in purely physical material systems. For instance, in the purely material realm, there is a strong tendency for all organized systems to break up and become less orderly with time. All systems are governed by the Second Law of Thermodynamics which insists that entropy, or disorderliness within any system, shall increase with time and that energy shall become less and less available. Everything gets into more probable, more mixed up states. This applies to every material system, and living systems are taken to be material systems. But living systems seem to be able to cheat this law in an odd sort of way. All the biosystems have found a way, each in their own fashion, to *use* the degradation of energy in order to build up, rather than destroy orderliness. They have found a way to interrupt and subvert the entropy-increasing system and use it to create ever more high-level, orderly, complex and elaborate forms.

Somehow they are able to exercise something very like intelligence. They use the energy that arises from the degradation of order to build higher levels of order. They do this through the possession of the power of intelligent choice. They behave as if they had a preference for a certain form – the form of the given creature. They make the choices which favour the survival or the copying of that form. They avoid the choices which would favour its breakup and dispersal – its normal fate under the power of the Second Law of Thermodynamics. But there is one kind of change that living forms accept: progressive or evolutionary change, the kind of change which enables them *even better to preserve their form in future*. This is the name of the life game. To preserve form with minimum change through time. To do that ever more efficiently is what evolution is all about.

The ladder of life and intelligence

In my book *The Future of Intelligence* I wrote about the steps up the ladder of life. You can rank the observable entities in the universe on an advancing series, going up the scale. We start with the most transient and unstable forms of energy, electromagnetic waves. We proceed to a more slightly more stable form of energy, the fundamental particles, starting with the most transient, which lasts for nanoseconds, and finishing with the really stable particles, protons. Then we come to cooperative combinations of fundamental particles. These are the atoms: some are unstable, some are more stable.

Once again they are organized assemblies of fundamental particles – protons, neutrons, electrons. Then we get molecules, organized combinations of atoms, and we have matter. The least stable form is a gas, then a liquid, then solids and finally periodic crystals.

The next step is a giant one. We get aperiodic crystals (those which can carry information such as DNA). Now we have a system that can preserve form through time in an intelligent way. It has a memory; that is what a genome (the set of genes) is.

Now we come to living forms: protozoa, single cells, organized combinations of molecules. Next we have metazoa and metaphyta, organized combinations of cells (animals and plants). Then we come to more and more organized combinations of animals, such as swarms, schools, herds, flocks and tribes of men.

Then we reach an even more complex form, cooperative combinations of human groups in large organizations – nations, cultures etc – or symbiotic, cooperating combinations of animals and plants in stable ecosystems.

As we go up the scale we observe these progressive changes:

1. The entities become more ordered and form larger combinations.
2. The combinations are more stable, last longer and are more faithfully replicated.
3. Their arrangement or form becomes more complex and less probable.
4. The useful (usable) energy available to the system becomes greater.

5. The number of forms proliferates and diverges, competing for living space.
6. The differing forms show symbiosis, mutual adaptation and cooperation into larger units.
7. The forms evince more ability to sense (know) the state of the universe and store the information.
8. They show increased power to control the future state of the universe by using the information sensed and stored.

The seventh and eighth points combined constitute intelligence in the advanced sense of the word.

The world communications net

If this update of the ladder of creation has any validity we on this tiny Earth are at a very exciting stage along this continuum. We have reached an extraordinary discontinuity. We should have expected the divergence of mankind's many peoples and cultures to have led to a patchwork of competitive subspecies.

But what has happened is the emergence of an enormous interacting, extremely complex, communications system whose connective tentacles have penetrated the developed nations very deeply. The financial, commercial and industrial markets are only a small part of this. The network of interactive communications includes the news network which spans the planet, and the international cultural, scientific, artistic and all the other linkage systems which span the modern word. Hardly any section of humanity is completely unaffected by the operations of this network. It is as though the peoples and institutions in many places were acting like the neurons of a single world brain which had developed from their interconnectedness. Amazingly, against all precedent in previous large civilizations, this astonishing communications system is a unity without a commanding centre.

There is no Caesar, king, khan, shah, emperor or president in charge. Yet it continues in a stable interacting way and it appears to optimize outcomes much like a living thing. People talk about an alien intelligence coming to Earth. Maybe another supervening intelligence is already here, called into existence by the intelligent interaction of billions of human minds, in the way they behave, what they read, where they go, what they buy, sell, invest, spend and save. It is the enormous development and elaboration of something first noticed by Adam Smith, which he called an engine (today he would have described it as a computer). He saw the intelligent, hidden hand of the market as something autonomous. He noted how the price mechanism and liberal trade practices brought people in far lands who had never heard of one another into an automatic and self-adjusting cooperation in order to supply one another's needs. He also observed that self-interest was the motivating force that drove his engine.

He did not waste words condemning human greed but showed how an open system could put it to work to drive the production and distribution system.

What we see today is that the whole of the biosphere of the Earth has come under the influence of this system. It has grown and spread, and has, to some extent, penetrated every social system, continent, nation and culture in a very short time.

The sheer volume of international traffic in communication is unimaginable. Through every channel – computer network, phone, fax, telex, radio, television, post, press and cable – an enormous parallel processing information exchange is directing, sending, processing and receiving trillions of bytes of information in an intricate, unfathomable pattern to all parts of planet Earth. As a result we in the rich part of the world get the newspaper, the brand of coffee, the exact kind of bread, eggs, cheese, wine and all the other highly specified articles and services we need or like or think we do. We are all induced, without any compulsion, to do what needs to be done, so that what is called for is supplied or delivered with regularity and reliability.

We grumble at the slightest error. This works well in all the places where this great network operates effectively and freely. These are, by and large, the prosperous places. But there are still about a billion people, according to the UN, who are living in sickness, because of undernourishment and real (not relative) want. They live in areas where, for various reasons this great world brain, this global communications net, has penetrated only weakly. Much of Africa below the Sahara, much of Asia and South America have such a subsistence economy on a large scale. Watching the growth and spread of the global information net and market it seems likely that, if it is not prevented by stupidity, the network will spread further into these areas during the next millennium.

Competitive co-operation

An important aspect of the ladder of life is the way in which two apparently antagonistic aspects are beneficially combined. The creatures on this earth exist in feeding chains. The plants have learned the trick of using the energy of sunlight to construct themselves out of minerals, water and carbon dioxide from the air. They excrete oxygen. We animals eat the plants and one another, and we use the excreted oxygen to get the energy from our food. And the little animals are eaten by bigger ones and those by yet bigger ones, all the way up the millions of food chains. It sounds like a 'dog eat dog' business all round. And there is no doubt that at all levels it is highly competitive. There is competition between and within most species for food, water, space, mates and resources of all kinds at all levels. Evolution is the way the species become what they are and evolution involves competition. Yet there is also symbiosis. There are many regulators of competition and many examples of creatures which fall into a cooperative or symbiotic life-style. Even the relationships of prey and predator slot into stable patterns which ensure the survival of both.

Mankind has been competitive and warlike for most of his history, but he is capable of creating fairly peaceful societies which last for a time. What works well is a pattern which accommodates the cooperative, social side of man's nature with the competitive side. If we compete for status and wealth and honour in our group it may be bad, but it is vastly better than competing militarily for life or death. Trying to suppress competition altogether does not seem to work. But to compete in trying to meet the needs of others (the market) or in careful regulated games and sports seems an intelligent and useful way to turn that side of our nature to good use.

Further up the ladder of life?

What happens if we try to peer up that ladder of life and intelligence to the few rungs ahead of us? Long ago life invaded the sea and filled it with a million teeming forms. It then invaded and occupied the land and filled every available place with another set of forms. We can now see that it is open to modern man to take life off Earth and seed the solar system with it. Is it not inevitable in the end that some men, some time, somewhere, will want to do that? Is it conceivable that there will be any way to stop such adventurers?

Intelligence in orbit

We are not quite sure but we are fairly certain that there is no other life, especialy intelligent life, in the solar system. So just consider the outrageous possibility that the long-term future of mankind lies beyond our earthly skies. If that is true it must also be true that the high-flyers, the very bright among us, will be greatly needed in orbits other than our own. 'Moving out' can solve the problem of overpopulation on a limited biosphere. A new biosphere in orbit around the Sun would take some time to overload. Those of us who favour planting the solar system with life and intelligence will need to find the superintelligent wherever they may be hiding in the lost corners of our complex societies. We shall need to make sure that they are offered the kind of education and training which can best develop their powers. We shall have to expect from them, and persuade them to expect from themselves, a greater contribution to the 'great adventure' than most can provide. We shall have to see that they are fully informed of the extra work and trouble they will have to invest in their education and preparation to serve. We shall want them to see the general advantage of it. We shall also need to motivate them personally. We shall be unwise if we rely too much on altruism (except, of course, in times of great social stress, such as wars and revolutions). In other words we shall have to revert to the Victorian habit of valuing, respecting and *rewarding* mental excellence when it can be persuaded to accept the rigours of advanced study and supernormal contribution, taking on more difficult, more responsible work and doing it well.

Other intelligences

I hope we are not the only intelligence in the universe. It would be a bit lonely if we were. And it would be a dreadful responsibility: the huge task of spreading the message of comprehension around the billions of galaxies would be ours.

There is no evidence at all of any other intelligence and some cosmologists are pessimistic because they reckon that there has been time enough since the Big Bang to develop creatures able to send us signals. And there are no signals. But I take the view that it would be anthropocentric (biased towards mankind) to believe that there is no other cognitive intelligence anywhere.

What does seem likely however is that the first 'alien intelligence' experienced by mankind will be created by mankind.

I concede that artificial intelligence as a possibility has been wildly oversold up till now. The problems are formidable and progress is so far slow. But if, as biologists believe, our biological forbears, using blind chance mutations, have evolved an effective brain, it seems likely that, given time, guided by good science and intelligence and starting with working models at hand, the trick can be done again, working with other materials, artificial or even biological. I think it would be extremely risky to put money on the idea that the quest for a man-made mind was bound to be disappointed.

My friend, Professor John Good, says that there is bound to be an intelligence explosion. If undirected evolution can produce intelligence, he says, then intelligent creatures will be forced by mutual competition to produce higher intelligences, then those higher intelligences will be able to produce even higher intelligences, and so on.

If we put our hope in mankind's ability to cooperate to limit the development of a rival intelligence we may be backing a loser. If we cannot cooperate enough to avoid dreadful destructive wars and conflicts, can we guarantee that no one will see and seize the chance to develop better brains to beat the competition? And once that race has begun . . . Look at the nuclear arms race. It would be hard to think of anything less constructive, or less intelligent. So we had better get ready to face the competition of both alien and native intelligence. That means finding our best competitors, our brightest human beings and giving them the best education and training we can procure.

Further Reading

N. BLOCK and G. DWORKIN (eds), *The IQ Controversy* (Quartet Books, 1977)

S. BRIDGES, *Gifted Children and the Brentwood Experiment* (1969)

H.J. EYSENCK, *The Scientific Study of Personality* (Routledge and Kegan Paul, 1952)
Know Your Own IQ (Penguin, 1969)
The Structure of Human Personality (Methuen, 1970)

A. FLEW, *Power to the Parents: Reversing Educational Decline* (Sherwood Press, 1987)

J.B.S. HALDANE, *Quantitative Measurements of Rates of Evolution* (1949)

A. HEIM, *Intelligence and Personality* (Penguin, 1970)

R.J. HERRNSTEIN, *IQ in the Meritocracy* (Allen Lane, 1973)

A.R. JENSEN, *Educability and Group Differences* (Methuen, 1976)

L.J. KAMIN, *The Science and Politics of IQ* (Penguin, 1977)

K. POPPER, *The Logic of Scientific Discovery* (Hutchinson, 1959)

V. SEREBRIAKOFF, *The Future of Intelligence* (Parthenon Publications, 1986)
A Guide to Intelligence and Personality Testing (Parthenon Publications, 1987)
Mensa: The Society for the Highly Intelligent (Constable, 1985)

L.M. TERMAN and M.N. ODEN, *The Gifted Children at Mid Life* (Stanford University Press, 1959)

S. WISEMAN, *Readings in Human Intelligence* (University Paperbacks, 1972)